This book belongs to:

_____

_____

_____

_____

If found, PLEASE be so kind and return it.

The reward is:

_____

Dominik Spenst

The 6-Minute

D I A R Y

A book that will change your life

UrBestSelf

Our Newsletter: *The Mindful Three*
Every two weeks, three exquisite tips on how to live a
simpler and more mindful life on *createurbestself.com*

For more daily inspiration and motivation
follow us on Instagram **@createurbestself**
#6minutediary

For questions or suggestions:
createurbestself.com

ISBN: 978-3-9818450-1-3
Copyright © 2016 Dominik Spenst

UrBestSelf GmbH
Aslaner Straße 3, 33100 Paderborn
Germany

13th Edition: August 2020

**We print books and plant trees in return: to reduce carbon dioxide emissions,
we support the *Evers-ReForest* initiative in growing new forests.**

Made & Bound with Love in Germany.

"

You will never change your life until you change something you do daily. The secret of your success is found in your daily routine.

JOHN C. MAXWELL

Contents

Your
Diamond Mine

... a short story with a big message.

One day, a Persian farmer named Al Hafed hears of diamonds for the first time in his life. A wise priest tells him about other farmers who became rich after discovering diamond mines: "A single diamond, no larger than the tip of your thumb, is worth a hundred farms," he tells the farmer who then decides to sell his farm in order to search for diamonds himself. For the rest of his life, Al Hafed wanders through Africa searching for diamond mines – in vain. His body exhausted and his spirit broken, he finally gives up his futile quest, and in his despair drowns himself in the ocean.

Back at the farm Al Hafed had sold, the new owner leads his camel to a shallow stream on the farm. He is surprised to discover something shiny at the bottom of the stream. As the new owner reaches into the water, he discovers a glittering black rock, which he takes home where he places it on the mantelpiece by his fireplace.

A few days later, the wise priest pays him a visit, as he wants to meet Al Hafed's successor. When he catches sight of the rock on the mantelpiece, he is left speechless. The farmer tells him where he has found the rock a few days earlier and that there are similar rocks to be found all over the stream. The priest knows better: "That is not a rock. It's an unpolished rough diamond, actually one of the biggest diamonds I've ever seen!" The stream that used to belong to Al Hafed became one of the most lucrative diamond mines of all time, known as the Golconda mine.
– freely told following *The Acres of Diamonds* by Russell H. Cornwell

So what is the message behind this little story about Al Hafed's unsuccessful quest? Actually it is pretty clear: Had Al Hafed appreciated the things he already possessed in his life at that point, he would have recognised the treasures which were already on his own piece of land.

The same applies to us: The biggest wealth is contained within ourselves. We need to dig and burrow in our own acres because the diamonds are hidden inside us. If you look for your very own diamond mine, you will find it. Pay conscious attention to the opportunities that come up in your day-to-day life and to the things your current life is already offering you.

What you are looking for is already inside you!

"

Your attitude about who you are and what you have is a very little thing that makes a very big difference.

THEODORE ROOSEVELT

6 Reasons

… why you'll love your 6 Minutes.

1. What you are holding in your hands right now is a simple and very effective tool that will guide you to become UrBestSelf

The 6-Minute Diary is not a Diary like any other. Its goal is to make you a happier and more fulfilled person in the long run by providing you with the simplest of methods.

At first glance, this may sound like a bold promise. Before you write your first Diary entry, though, you will get a comprehensive explanation of how you can reach precisely this goal by investing merely 6 Minutes a day. In order to fully benefit from the tool in your hand, you should carefully read the instructions before getting started. Once you have established the actual habit of using your *6-Minute Diary* on a daily basis, it can work wonders. With every day that you use it, you add another brick and thus build your first wall of happiness. One wall is quickly joined by several other walls, and before you know it, you've built yourself a beautiful and solid house of happiness. There are many books that promise you a happy and fulfilled life, but often these are exactly the kind of books that fail to deliver by not living up to their promises. They tend to tell you that there is a golden rule, one perfect path to happiness. 'The' single formula that obviously doesn't exist, since we are all so different and there is no one-size-fits-all solution. *The 6-Minute Diary*, in contrast, offers you the foundation and the building materials, so you can construct your house of happiness on your own. Day by day, you have the chance to decide how to build your house of happiness. With each Diary page that you fill in, you are putting your own individual mark on things – your personal fingerprint.

For 2.8 million years, every human being has been born with a preinstalled software: the survival software.[1] This ancient programme was responsible and essential for surviving – or being killed. Today, however, it is less useful as it keeps pushing the brain to look for things that are going wrong or that might present a threat to your survival.

It is always looking for whatever might hurt you, so you can either fight it or flee from it. As a result, your brain evolved to learn quickly from bad experiences but slowly from good ones.[2] For example, studies show that we can identify angry faces much faster than happy ones. Even if we see the angry faces so briefly (just a tenth of a second), that we are not able to consciously recognise them, the parts of our brain responsible for emotion and the formation of new memories get activated.[3] By contrast, the same study reveals that pictures of happy faces – also shown just for a tenth of a second – flow straight through the brain without recognition. Over and over again, psychologists find that our brain automatically triggers negative feelings because it reacts more quickly, persistently and strongly to bad things than to equivalent good things.[4] In line with this, the pain of loss is on average three to four times stronger than the joy of possessing that same thing.[5] This is why the experience of a broken heart causes more pain than the experience of being in a harmonious relationship causes happiness. Similarly, in financial transactions, the joy of gaining a certain amount of money is smaller than the pain of losing that same amount.[6] And in the same way, in marital interactions, it takes at least five good actions to make up for the damage of one bad action.[7] Your mind naturally overemphasises the negative and three decades of research about Positive Psychology (p.26) will certainly not change something that was evolutionary programmed into our brains for the last three million years.

Happiness and satisfaction? – Those are not your brain's major interests. Again, your brain is wired to take in the bad and ignore the good. For this reason, it is so much easier for most people to connect with somebody by gossiping or complaining and that's also why bad news spread much faster than good ones. It's why you cannot turn away when you see a car accident or somebody fighting. And it is also why you find yourself fixating on the one or two small criticisms although you received overwhelmingly positive feedback for something. From an evolutionary standpoint, it's just easier for us to focus on the negative. Pleasant emotional states such as contentment used to be potentially damaging in the raw fight for survival. Therefore, your mind is constantly identifying and magnifying potential threats which, in turn, results in a life filled with stress, irritation and anxiety. This unfortunate mechanism has allowed our species to be naturally good at surviving, but not at being happy. Those humans who were unhappy and insecure to a certain degree, were the ones best at innovating and surviving. It's survival of the fittest, not survival of the happiest and you can thank our caveman ancestors for this one.

66

Our brain has a negativity bias, which makes it like Velcro for the bad and Teflon for the good.

RICK HANSON

The good news is: You can actively change this and *The 6-Minute Diary* gives you many different ways to do that. What you need to do is to outwit your brain, counterbalance its ancient negativity and learn to see through the lies it tells you. Fortunately, science has proven that you can rewire your brain through proactive, and most importantly, daily repetition. As a counterweight for your negative emotions, you are therefore able to install a new programme by cultivating positive habits. This installation process is called neuroplasticity (p.34), and it takes an average of 66 days of daily performance before it is completed and a habit is internalised.[8] The key to success is continuity. Happiness is not a matter of luck or coincidence, but something you can learn step by step.

> *The most important trick to be happy is to realize that happiness is a choice that you make and a skill that you develop. You choose to be happy, and then you work at it.*
>
> NAVAL RAVIKANT

Are you grateful for what you have? And if so, do you express this gratitude regularly in a way in which it deserves to be expressed? When was the last time you felt genuine gratitude towards your partner or your best friend? When was the last time you told them just how grateful you are for the amazing things they do for you, rather than getting upset about the little things that bother you?

If you aren't grateful for what you have today, you won't be grateful for what you will get tomorrow or a week from now. And we're not talking about the parcel from Amazon, the flattering compliment or the anniversary celebration. We're talking about things that are part of your everyday life. It has been proven that focusing on appreciation every day, which means, focusing on what you ALREADY HAVE in your life, will make you feel happier and more satisfied in the long run. *The 6-Minute Diary* is designed in such a way that all you have to do is invest a few minutes every day in order to develop positive behaviour patterns and an optimistic attitude. It enables you to focus a lot more on the opportunities in your life rather than on the obstacles. If you want to feel good, you need to think accordingly. This is why one principle of *The 6-Minute Diary* is not to focus on the things that are missing or aren't working, but to consciously take into account what is already there, and what is actually working. In doing so, you make the positive aspects visible and practise developing constructive thoughts. The diary helps you to find the right balance between appreciation and further development, as well as between gratitude and achievement. It helps you learn to fully appreciate the Here and Now. You will see how gratitude can make you happier, and you are provided with a stage on which you can practise it daily. Gratitude is the magic spell that opens the door to all the opportunities your day has to offer. Or to put it into Mark Twain's words: "Give every day the chance to become the most beautiful day of your life."

2. No motivational gibberish, usual drivel or esoteric wishy-washy. The concept is based on scientific findings

This book makes no promises that aren't based on the results of the latest research in neuroscience and psychology, on ancient wisdom, actual experience and evidence-based practices. The groundwork for *The 6-Minute Diary* is provided by research of renowned psychologists and widely recognised scientists. You can thus save yourself the effort of going through hundreds of scientific publications to separate the useless research from the useful research. As you can see in the bibliography at the end, this job has already been done for you.

Everybody knows, however, that theoretical knowledge and practical application are two very different pairs of shoes. One may confidently assume that any physician knows a lot about nutrition and health. But does that mean that all physicians practise what they preach? Most likely not. The same goes for the positive effects of gratitude, an optimistic attitude, self-reflection and good habits in general. It is one thing to merely read and talk about these things, and another to actually integrate them into your life.

The great thing is: To put theory into practice, you don't need to spend any more money than you've already paid for this book! **You already hold a compact and effective tool in your hands, a tool that enables you to use the theoretical framework of Positive Psychology for your benefit – effectively and for the long term, in only 6 Minutes a Day.**

3. Your daily writing practice will come more easily than with any other diary

Have you ever witnessed someone putting in a lot of effort, trying to change something in his or her life? Losing ten pounds, adopting a healthier diet, getting more sleep, getting a head start on studying for an exam, being more affectionate in relationships… elaborate plans were made, but the relapse happened quickly and soon they fell into old patterns. Statistics suggest that you have experienced similar things: 92% of the people who want to quit smoking fail. 95% of the people who want to lose weight end up experiencing the infamous yo-yo effect, and a whopping 88% of the people who start a new year with resolutions ultimately don't implement any of them.[9] Why shouldn't the same thing be true for keeping a diary? At the beginning you are scribbling away, highly motivated, but that initial enthusiasm passes quickly, and the journaling project is literally shelved. The reasons for getting sidetracked are manifold: you're lacking a proper structure, the time you have to invest seems too much, or you didn't internalise the point of keeping a diary. *The 6-Minute Diary* systematically removes all these typical hurdles. It was designed to ensure that even those who aren't normally diarists are going to keep the ball rolling.

"

Nothing is particularly hard if you divide it into small jobs.

HENRY FORD

The structure of this Diary may seem rather simple at first sight, but is in fact thoroughly thought through, and will convince even critical readers once they have read the elaborate introduction. Especially the frequently mentioned excuse that time is scarce does not apply to *The 6-Minute Diary*. Splitting the daily time into three minutes in the morning and three before bedtime is an achievable task – even for the most creative excuse inventors amongst us.

The fixed times for writing in your Diary make it easier to establish a daily routine. Ideally, the Diary is your first impulse after getting up and your last impulse before going to sleep. A goal without a due date is nothing more than a dream. In this case, the goal is the maximisation of your personal happiness. Each morning and each evening from now on, you have a tiny appointment, and this will ensure that you are getting closer to the goal, one tiny step after another, slowly but surely.

"I can type just as well, so why am I supposed to use pen and paper?" – That's because the good old-fashioned pen is mightier than the keyboard. Notes shift from the paper pad to your computer screen, tasks are jotted down in the to-do list app, and the fountain pen has not been touched since primary school. And yet, psychologists have shown again and again that writing things down transforms us in fundamental ways. We understand things better if we write them down, and they remain longer in our memory than if we type them.[10] There is even some evidence that you can speed up the healing process of physical injuries if you keep a Diary.[11] *The 6-Minute Diary* is not an app, but a book exclusively dedicated to a single purpose. It is a physical tool that allows you to use the all but forgotten benefits of pen and paper in your own favour.

4. You create a unique treasure chest of your memories

A Diary is like a good wine. If you put it aside for a while, it gathers maturity and can be enjoyed in its full glory. Imagine you have filled all the pages of *The 6-Minute Diary* and then put it away. If you take it from the shelf after several months or even years, you can take a priceless journey into the most exciting and emotional realms of your own memory. You will notice that you have come to see certain things in a completely different way than you used to. In hindsight, you realise why that is, and this way, you can follow the footsteps of your personal evolution. What you hold in your hands will then be a one-of-a-kind testimony to your former experiences, wishes, thoughts and perspectives. As the Roman poet Martial said almost 2000 years ago: "He lives two lives who relives his past with pleasure." Imagine your grandfather or your mother had written such a book themselves. What would they give to have such a matchless memento? What could be more exciting than possessing a book about yourself and your life? If you want to own a treasure chest filled with all your memories, you are most certainly on the right path now.

5. It is fun and it shows you exactly what makes you happy

The main point of the Diary entries is that you actually feel them (see p.62, Tip 2). Take two minutes to think of something you are grateful for, maybe a precious experience in your life or a moment you particularly cherish. Close your eyes as soon as you have thought of something. Do it now and not some other time... How do you feel now? Take a few seconds to consciously feel the emotion. Gratitude is the counterpart to all negative emotions. It has the power to amplify your positive experiences and to intensify what is good in your life. Since mental engagement with positive things is naturally enjoyable, writing in this Diary will automatically do you good and will involve a certain fun factor as well. In a similar fashion, The Weekly Challenges and especially *The 5 Weekly Questions* add excitement, variety and entertainment. Yet, *The 6-Minute Diary* is much more than just a feel-good book. This book is not written by a self-help guru with an utterly charming smile. It is also not telling you to make your dreams come true by saying "I'm a champion" to your reflection in the bathroom mirror. There already is a host of voices ready to tell you that banning the word "impossible" from your vocabulary will help you make your life a succession of moments of happiness. Instead, some of the daily and weekly questions in this Diary go deeper and may get down to the nitty-gritty. It is not your answers to those questions which count the most but rather the precious moments when you really dive deep and search for those answers. The more you get involved with the questions, the more you will benefit from this book.

What makes you happy? Being able to answer this question might well be more important today than ever before, considering the multitude of possible paths life can take. *The 6-Minute Diary* is a unique tool to help you find out what actually makes you happy because it asks the right questions, every single day. It's a matter of common knowledge that a clever question is already half the battle.

6. You learn to emancipate your inner happiness from outer circumstances

Confucius said: "You have two lives, and the second begins when we realise we only have one." Asked whether he had already experienced such a turning point in his life, the successful American founder and investor Naval Ravikant replied as follows: "I struggled for a lot of my life to have certain material and social successes, and when I achieved those material and social successes or at least beyond the point where they didn't matter as much to me anymore, I realised that my peer group and a lot of the people who were around me – the people who had achieved similar successes and were on their way to achieving more and more successes – just didn't seem all that happy. And also in my case there was never a permanent gain in happiness after reaching new goals, I very quickly got used to anything. So it led me to the conclusion – which seems trite – that happiness is internal. And so then that set me on a path of starting to work more on my internal self and realising that all real success is internal and has very little to do with external circumstances."[12]

Naval Ravikant's experience is by no means singular. Most of us think that we will be happier IF we have more money, IF we live in a cooler place, IF we meet our Mr or Mrs Right or IF we get our dream job. And yet, it is not necessary at all to wait for the next great event to be more grateful and happier on a long-term basis. Because every time you achieve one of those goals, you will realise that nothing has really changed. You are still the same person. It is very rare that external circumstances make you happier IN THE LONG RUN. There are many widely recognised studies to prove this[13], and most probably your own life experience is also going to back up this claim. This type of thinking – namely that everything depends on the next IF of life – is what psychologists call conditional happiness and most of us are conditioned to think this way. The IF is the enemy of your contentment. Like the horizon, you can walk endlessly and will never reach the IF because there is always that one more thing you'll need to do to be extra-exceptionally happy. Honestly, how many times have you thought: If I achieve this or that goal I will be happier? And how many times did you actually feel that afterwards you were happier for a sustained period of time?

Today, pay attention to how often you're looking for more and therefore are neglecting the present moment. How often do you want the future to unfold exactly as you expect it to, instead of enjoying the present moment? Take your chance on happiness here and now. **Starting today, take the time to celebrate the small moments of happiness in your life. Take the time to appreciate and cherish the small successes in your day. When was the last time you celebrated one of your successes? If you can't do that, it's unlikely that you will celebrate the big ones.**

The path to a happier life is not a secret recipe that is reserved exclusively for Buddhist monks. In only 6 Minutes a Day, you can develop a more positive attitude that will help you emancipate your happiness from the "IFs" of life. Read on and find out for yourself.

66

Yesterday's the past, tomorrow's the future, but today is a gift. That's why it's called the present.

BILL KEANE

Thank You!

After two wonderful semesters of studying abroad, filled with travelling the most beautiful countries of Asia, the return to my hometown in Germany was just around the corner. To give that exciting year its finishing touch, I went on the first solo trip of my life: Freshly arrived in Cambodia, I set off to a motorbike rental where I met a seemingly like-minded guy. We decided to join forces and rode to a viewpoint in the surrounding area. Taking in the magnificent view of unspoiled countryside, I slowed down approaching a crossroads, when – at an estimated speed of 50 mph – my acquaintance suddenly dashed into my leg from behind. While I flew through the air and tumbled over countless times, he landed more fortunately, looked at me for a few seconds, and flew the coop... So I was lying there: covered with blood, alone in the middle of nowhere in Cambodia, in the glaring sun at 35 degrees. Although I couldn't feel my lower body, I could see the flesh of my front leg with the entire shin bone showing – a sight that made me lose consciousness several times. A few natives approached the scene, but instead of helping, all they did was stare at me – one of them even started filming my leg with his phone. After what felt like an eternity, I saw a few policemen and felt a huge relief: *They are finally taking me to the hospital!* The officers, however, didn't say a single word to me and once they realised there were no bribes to collect, they calmly left the scene – unimpressed by my cries for help. It was only then when I really started to panic, because for the first time it occurred to me that they might actually let me bleed to death. As the group of natives was getting smaller, I suddenly felt somebody lifting my head from behind and heard a kind voice saying: "What's your name?". I replied and he said: "Hi Dominik, my name is Doug and I will get you the hell out of here, but you have to stop looking at your leg!" Doug was around 65 years old and from Australia. If you are reading this, Doug: Thank you for saving my life!

What followed were 16 weeks in hospital, 12 surgeries and the uncertainty as to whether I could keep my left leg or not. After each successive surgery, the situation remained unchanged or became worse. For somebody who had barely ever gone a single week without sports in his life, the thought of losing a leg was crushing. Though this should have caused my spirits to sink lower and lower, I kept getting comments such as: "How come you're so upbeat?" or "You act as if nothing happened." I'm not a good actor; I simply noticed that my attitude had started to dissociate itself more and more from the outer circumstances – the "IFs" of life. Before the accident, I was constantly obsessed with making a career and getting outside validation: If I make it to the top 5% of my graduate class, all doors will be open for me. *If I work for this and that prestigious company, a house and family will follow automatically* (although the wife was yet to be found). While none of these IF's actually made me happier, I was still trapped in their treadmill... and had it not been for the accident, I would most probably still be chasing the same outside successes today.

Do you remember the quote from Naval Ravikant on the last page? His realisation, namely that happiness can primarily be influenced from the inside, suggested itself to me in hospital with each passing day. That process was no coincidence but the result of sustained daily gratitude and self-reflection which helped me understand two essential things: On the one hand, I recognized that my thinking patterns stood in my own way as I was endlessly postponing my happiness with every new goal that I set for myself. On the other hand, it became clear that I did not give myself permission to be who I truly was because I was primarily pursuing other people's goals – goals that had very little to do with my own values. Luckily, the experience of being hospitalised made me stop putting energy into wishing things were different and waiting for the next "IF" to happen. Rather than focusing on the bad things – which is quite easy when your world is confined to a hospital bed and toilet – I concentrated on the good things, which were still quite numerous: I still had another leg and despite the severe concussions, my brain was still working. My family along with my closest friends were there for me throughout the whole time and I even learned to appreciate the little treasures of everyday life in hospital. In a nutshell: I learned that real success is inner success and this attitude hasn't changed since then. I'm happier than I was before – and nowadays also back on my own feet.

Since the accident, I have not only spent thousands of hours studying the human psyche, but I also had the chance to gain insights into personal experiences from the pool of more than 700.000 6-Minute Diary users worldwide. In all this, I kept arriving at the same conclusion, namely that small habits have a huge impact. Since internalising and applying that seemingly trite insight, I've put all my energy into developing tools that help people answer the following two questions: What makes me happy? And: Which habits can bring more of that into my life? No matter which goals you want to reach, positive habits that you build up in small, realistic steps are the best way to get you there. The good news is: To put this into practice and build life-enriching habits, you don't need a traumatic wake-up-call. For me personally, a lot of great things would not have happened without that potentially devastating accident. You are holding one of those great things in your hands right now.

Let's come to some of the more classic acknowledgments: First off, thank you to the German readers who with their great feedback motivated me to write this English version. Thank you to the sources of inspiration that I've never met face to face: Robert Greene, Tony Robbins, Maria Popova, Jonathan Haidt, Alex Ikonn, Ryan Holiday, Tim Schlenzig and Martin Seligman. A huge THANK YOU to my family and my closest friends. I keep being reminded of how important these people are and where I would be today if it wasn't for them. And last but not least, thank YOU! Thank you for joining this journey towards a more mindful and fulfilled life!

> **It is not the outer circumstances that change a life, but the inner changes which manifest themselves in life.**
> WILMA THOMALLA

Quick Overview

... of how to best use your 6-Minute Diary.

Morning Routine

❶ Morning gratitude (p.44)
Write down three things you're grateful for, or one thing plus three reasons why you're grateful for this.

❷ How you make your day great (p.50)
Focus on the opportunities and possibilities of the day. What are your goals and priorities for today? What are the concrete actions that will enable you to take steps in the right direction?

❸ Positive affirmation (p.53)
Draw a picture of how you see yourself today or in the future. Define yourself as the person you want to be.

Evening Routine

❹ Your good deed today (p.57)
Even the smallest act of kindness can make someone else happy. A good deed serves to give you a sustained sense of happiness in return.

❺ Room for improvement (p.58)
You want to grow and develop continually. What have you learned today? What opportunities for improvement do you see?

❻ Today's moments of happiness (p.60)
Each day is filled with small moments of happiness and success. Meet them with your eyes wide open, seize them and hold on to them.

Weekly Routine

Your 5 Weekly Questions (p.22)
This section contains a lot of questions that you've probably never asked yourself before – all aimed at getting to know yourself better.

Your Weekly Challenge (p.24)
This is where you leave your comfort zone in order to do something for others or yourself.

Example Page

... what your 6–Minute routine could look like.

MTWTFS Ⓢ <u>20/05/2021</u>

❶ I'm grateful for…

1. <u>the rays of sunshine on my skin</u>
2. <u>the yummy breakfast I'm about to prepare</u>
3. <u>my amazing friends who enrich my life</u>

❷ This is how I make today great

<u>I will exercise because I want to feel fit and healthy</u>
<u>I will set aside one hour to work on my current project, so I can feel</u>
<u>productive and self–determined</u>
<u>I am going to meditate to feel more at peace with myself</u>

❸ Positive affirmation

<u>I'm in control of my attitude and I decide to be strong and confident</u>

Quote of the day or Challenge of the week

❹ My good deed today

<u>I held the door for someone</u>
<u>I gave the barista a genuine smile</u>

❺ How I'll improve

<u>I'm going to call Mum and ask her how she's doing</u>
<u>I won't drink coffee after 2 p.m. anymore</u>

❻ Great things I experienced today

1. <u>Ana said I have a great sense of humour</u>
2. <u>I managed to reach all my goals for the day</u>
3. <u>Oliver from work gave me this amazing Italian recipe</u>

21

More than just a
Diary

... what the weekly and monthly routines have to offer.

The 5 Weekly Questions – The truth about you

*It is easier to judge the mind of a man
by his questions rather than his answers.*
PIERRE-MARC-GASTON

Everyone wants answers. We tend to believe that answers tell us how to fix things and at best, how to live more happily. Especially our school and work system have conditioned us to think this way: From exam to exam and from task to task, we are taught to focus on results. We get good grades for the "right" answers and our bosses pat us on our backs for delivering good results. But life is not just about the end goal, it is about the journey – with all its little detours, humps and bumps. The fact that our society attaches such a great value to answers and results, is translated to our personal lives as well.

All too often, we either do not ask ourselves the appropriate questions or we do not ask them often enough because we're too focused on a quick fix and instant gratification. Answers make us believe there's no need to go further as we already discovered everything, whereas questions push us to think outside the box and to discover new things. The process of bringing up and engaging in a question is what ultimately leads us to advancement and growth. In line with this, Ray Dalio, founder of the most successful hedge fund in the world, says: "Smart people are the ones who ask the most thoughtful questions, as opposed to thinking they have all the answers. Great questions are a much better indicator of future success than great answers."[14] Thus, if you value learning, growing and moving forward, it is absolutely necessary to develop an appreciation for questions. With *The 5 Weekly Questions*, you are heading in that exact direction.

The 5 Weekly Questions are different and new each week. They are either profound, interesting, entertaining, inspiring or a mix of all of the above. If you don't like certain questions, feel free to ignore them or even better: just mark the question and give it a second chance a few weeks later. Try asking yourself where that feeling of resistance is coming from, because sometimes the questions that cause you discomfort are the ones that will give you the most valuable insights. Also keep in mind that – especially for the deeper questions – there isn't the one and only answer.

"

Successful people ask better questions, and as a result, they get better answers.

TONY ROBBINS

Whether in science, in your professional or your personal life, most answers are temporary and change over time, while the fundamental questions stay the same. Therefore, some of your answers today might be different from the ones you would give in a month or in a year. What matters most with *The 5 Weekly Questions* are not your answers, but rather the precious moments when you listen to yourself – while contemplating and searching for those answers.

> *To get to know yourself a little,*
> *you need to study yourself a little.*
> IWAN SERGEJEWITSCH TURGENEW

The happiest people are the ones who discover their own nature and match the way they live to this nature. A great part of *The 5 Weekly Questions* revolves around exploring this exact nature to help you build a foundation for a fulfilled life. If you allow yourself to truly engage with the questions, you will get a unique glimpse behind the scenes of your personality. The questions give you food for thought, they challenge you to engage in some serious soul-searching and reflect your current state of mind – all geared towards diving deep and gaining clarity about your fears, desires and goals. You dig up repressed and forgotten things from the farthest corners of your consciousness and uncover surprising things about yourself. You're looking at yourself from new perspectives, which will guide your thoughts in new directions, enable you to open doors that were closed before and to open your mind.

The Weekly Challenge – Leave Your Comfort Zone

Each week, *The 6-Minute Diary* provides you with a unique challenge that invites you to do something good for others or yourself. At the beginning, meeting the challenges might seem difficult, but in the long term, they serve to increase your well-being. Nature programmed your survival software to save effort and energy. As a result, it is very sceptical towards the new and unfamiliar. It usually rejects the new because the subconscious mind associates the new with threat. That is the reason why you'd rather stay snuggled up in your cosy comfort zone. You want to remain where everything is familiar, where you can minimise stress and risk. In the anxiety-free space where everything is more or less safe and predictable. You want to have an athletic body but you don't want to go to the gym or withstand the temptation of unhealthy treats. You prefer to dream about walking down the aisle with your perfect partner, instead of taking the first step and going on an actual date.

> *You never change your life until you step out*
> *of your comfort zone; change begins at*
> *the end of your comfort zone.*
> ROY T. BENNETT

Since you bought this Diary, it's very likely that you are more open towards new things than the average person. If you accept the challenges and thus allow for a confrontation with new experiences, you will learn, stay flexible and evolve. The challenges force you to jump over your own shadow. While in reality that defies the laws of physics and is therefore impossible, your mind is certainly capable of achieving this. Like Tim Ferriss, the voice behind the most downloaded podcast in the world, said: "A person's success in life can usually be measured by the number of uncomfortable situations he or she is willing to have."[15] Whether it's for being more successful in your job, your relationships, your spiritual or fitness ambitions: your goals and your comfort zone don't live on the same street; they don't even have the same post code. Therefore, it is convenient but not good to take the convenient as the good. Like any genuine progress in life, your personal growth takes place outside your comfort zone. You practically jump out of the mental nest of your comfort and convenience – and nobody will benefit more from this than you.

The Weekly Habit-Tracker – Make good resolutions become solid habits

Good habits are of paramount importance for a good life. This is why we dedicated an entire chapter to the subject of habits. It is also the reason why The Weekly Habit-Tracker is part of the Diary (p.69). No matter what it is that you want to change in your life, the best way to implement changes on a sustainable basis is: via good habits – habits which you build up in small and realistic steps. With the help of The Weekly Habit-Tracker, you have a unique tool to establish good habits and likewise, to get rid of unwanted ones.

The Monthly Check – Your personal snapshot

It is only the smartest people who use their perspicacity not just to judge other people, but also themselves.
MARIE VON EBNER-ESCHENBACH

Overall mood, mindfulness, eating healthy, finances, having fun,… where do you see yourself in the different areas of your life? In this section, you keep an eye on the big picture, which allows you to compare how different aspects of your life are changing over time. In the beginning, you take stock to see where you are and over the following months, you can see how the different areas of your life are evolving. You can take a quick look now (p.68). If there's a category that you feel you cannot relate to, simply leave it blank or cross it out and replace it with another aspect that you feel might be missing. Don't hesitate to make this Diary your very own and add your unique fingerprint.

The
Fundamentals

... the theoretical principles behind this practical book.

The Fundamentals of this Diary are split into three parts: Positive Psychology, Habits and Self-Reflection. Research in the field of Positive Psychology forms the theoretical groundwork for this Diary, but we also cover the basic principles of habits and self-reflection. If you learn to apply these principles correctly, you can achieve pretty much whatever you want in your life. Deep down, you may already know some of these things, but it's all too easy to forget them in the daily hassles of work, social responsibilities and your own needs. The Fundamentals help you to understand and internalise these principles in theory, while the Diary lets you practise their application on a daily basis.

Fundamentals 1: Positive Psychology

... the science that makes people happier.

What is Positive Psychology? – Psychologists haven't always studied happiness. In fact, until the late 1990s, research in the field of psychology centered almost exclusively on the negative aspects of human life. The focus was on the treatment of mental illnesses and on how people should cope with their greatest pains like depression or mental breakdowns. One of the main reasons for this is that psychology as a field of research has always been strongly dependent on governmental funding. Following World War II, this money went almost entirely into the treatment of mental illnesses that resulted from the war. The focus of psychology remained the same for the next 50 years. What was left out of the equation were the people who were not suffering from any sort of mental illness or disorder – people who were, for the most part relatively content with their lives. In short: "normal" people. Some sceptics might read this and think normal people are unhappy but that is just plain wrong. The statistics speak for themselves: Drawing on a combination of 146 different studies, a total of 188,000 adults (including 18,000 college students) from 16 countries were polled and the vast majority of these people self-identified as "quite happy."[16] As usual, exceptions prove the rule: Times of war or political oppression such as apartheid in South Africa or the genocide in Cambodia paint a different picture, but if you walk through the streets today, you may safely assume that most people you encounter are rather happy than unhappy. The same studies show that happiness is evenly distributed throughout different age groups, cultures, sexes, incomes and countries.

How do you make people happier?

So what makes life worth living? What improves people's well-being and how can they create a life they really love? How can you make people happier and more fulfilled, instead of merely repairing defects and deficits? If you could measure the subjective well-being of a person on a scale from -10 (utterly miserable) to +10 (super happy), the main question of Positive Psychology would be: How can you increase a person's well-being from 1 to 4 or from 5 to 8, instead of dragging it up from -8 to -3 or from -2 to 0?

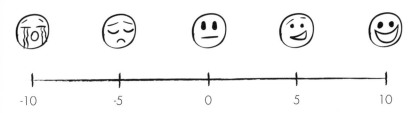

Simply put: How can you cause thriving flowers to blossom and flourish, instead of withering ones to thrive? Positive Psychology is the study of human flourishing, the science of what is needed for a good and meaningful life.

The good life needs a separate explanation

The general assumption used to be that the recovery from a -5 to a 0 was equal to the attainment of well-being and happiness. Studies have shown that this is a logical fallacy. Our intuition would agree: If a person is no longer suffering from depression, that doesn't mean they rise and shine every morning, looking forward to the day ahead. A happy life doesn't automatically result from a cure of whatever it was that the person in question suffered from. Put in a different way: A zero on the scale is fundamentally different from everything greater than zero. Hence, the good life needs its own research and a separate explanation. It's no use simply flipping the theoretical principles of traditional (negative) psychology around. For this reason, Positive Psychology doesn't orient its research towards illnesses and disorders but instead focuses on people's well-being by researching its sustained and sustainable amplification.

The time has finally arrived for a science that seeks to understand positive emotion, build strength and virtue, and provide guide-posts for finding what Aristotle called the "good life".
MARTIN SELIGMAN

Everyone can solve the happiness equation!

Positive Psychology stands and falls with the reliability of the scientific findings it is based on. The clarity of those findings has been impressive so far. Although for almost every theory there's also an opposing theory, until now there have been no scientifically proven counterviews for the key messages of Positive Psychology. To put it simply, Positive Psychology has successfully demonstrated the following points:

1. Gratitude is fundamentally important to a person's well-being.
2. The richness of life is more important than the riches of life; material factors such as wealth or social status are not decisive for personal happiness in the long run.
3. A person's relationships are of monumental importance for their subjective well-being.
4. **Happiness can be learned. It's possible to acquire happiness; it's not a matter of fate or good or bad fortune.**

This Diary does not equal a pair of rose-coloured glasses

The 6-Minute Diary is meant to help you establish a habit of focusing on the things that make you happy. In addition to that, it intends to help you find out what these things are. The goal of the Diary is not to make you see things through rose-coloured glasses and negate or repress negative feelings of any kind, but to see life through a more optimistic lens. Putting lipstick on every pig in your life and pretending everything is unicorns and rainbows is not a sustainable approach. Delusional positive thinking is never a long-term solution, which is why the Evening Routine of the Diary contains a section on how you plan to improve yourself.

> *You cannot tailor-make the situations in life, but you can tailor-make your attitudes to fit those situations.*
> ZIG ZIGLAR

The mottos are: put the focus on opportunities, not on obstacles. A good portion of optimism will provide you with hope and a dash of pessimism prevents you from exaggerating complacency. Enough realism will help you distinguish between the things you can influence and those you have no control over.

Embrace your sadness to appreciate your happiness

Do you know someone who, no matter the situation or the circumstances, just seems super happy all the time? It is very likely that the inner life of this person looks very different from what it appears to be – since denying negative emotions leads to even graver and more long-lasting negative emotions in the long-run.[17] For instance, have you ever tried to push a beach ball underwater? This endeavour is about as effective as trying to suppress your feelings permanently. It takes a lot of effort to keep the ball underwater, yet it has little effect as the ball will return to the surface anyway. Just like beach balls want to find their way back to the surface, your feelings simply want to be felt.

> *Even a happy life cannot be without a measure of darkness, and the word happy would lose its meaning if it were not balanced by sadness.*
> CARL GUSTAV JUNG

Our contemporary society is shaped by a consumer culture and by social media with central themes like: "I'm so happy, I'm in love, I'm sexy!", "I'm special and unique because I'm doing something different!" or "Hey! Look at me! My life is way cooler than yours!" An entire generation has grown up to believe that negative experiences – fear, anxiety, sorrow, guilt, etc. – are not okay at all. The crucial point, however, is that without negative emotions, we can't experience positive ones. There is no yang without yin, no courage without fear, no light without darkness, no life without death, no relaxation without tension, and no happiness without sadness. To feel happy, a certain measure of negative emotions is absolutely necessary and even healthy.

The sooner you accept that you can't avoid sadness and pain completely, the sooner you will stop avoiding your personal happiness. You cannot create eternally perfect happiness, but you can maximise it. You cannot lead a perfect life, but you can live a good life. *The 6-Minute Diary* will not put you into a state of pure happiness, but if you use it as it is meant to be used, you will be happier than before. You will know yourself better, love yourself more deeply, and be closer to your goals.

> **"**
> *You cannot protect yourself from sadness without protecting yourself from happiness.*
> JONATHAN SAFRAN FOER

Fundamentals 2: Habits

... the high road to Ur BestSelf.

> *Men's natures are alike.*
> *It is their habits that separate them.*
> CONFUCIUS

Human beings are creatures of habit. We make 95% of our daily decisions without making use of our conscious mind.[18] These decisions are made in milliseconds by our subconscious, governed by routine and automatisms. On average, 70% of our daily thoughts are identical with those of the day before and 40% of our behaviour is repeated every day, purely out of habit.[19] It is thus understandably hard to get the creature of habit to leave its rut.

Imagine the following scenario: A radio station starts a contest with the grand prize of £50,000. The radio host, Hailey Brooks, will call a random local telephone number at some point during the week. If you answer the phone with the host's name instead of your own, those £50,000 are yours. You are currently £45,000 in debt, so you could easily pay off your debt if you won the contest. The contest craze is all over the town and everyone is talking about it. You are lucky enough to have the week off and so far you've managed to answer each call with "This is Hailey Brooks" since Monday. Now it's Saturday evening, 8:57 p.m. and you're about to watch the next episode of Game of Thrones (GoT) on HBO. As you're preparing a tasty sandwich to munch on while watching GoT, the phone rings. The only thing on your mind is that you don't want to miss the beginning of the episode because of a stupid cold call. You hurry, pick up the phone and ... answer with your own name! Of course Hailey Brooks is on the other line and you don't win the £50,000. How on earth could that happen? The answer is very simple: Your inner creature of habit showed you once more who's the boss. No matter how much you could have used the 50 k, willingness and habit are two very different things!

A few days were not sufficient to change your habit and to free the creature from its habitual cage – its habitat. It actually takes approximately 66 days to achieve that, which will be explained in more detail later on. Roughly the same time frame applies to any other behaviour you want to change. This should make it obvious that you cannot steer your attitude to life in a more positive direction within the course of a few days. Similarly, *The 6-Minute Diary* will need more than a few days to take full effect on your life. Since it will accompany you for more than 66 days – in fact, for half a year – this gives you more than enough time to acquire or abandon any habit you want. In order for the transformation to be successful, it is necessary to take small steps rather than big ones. So start small but dream big, and watch how your habits will become part of you over time.

"

We first make our habits, and then our habits make us.

JOHN DRYDEN

Willpower is a limited resource

In the morning a man walks with his whole body,
in the evening, only with his legs.
RALPH WALDO EMERSON

Do you know those demanding days when you made a lot of decisions and come home in the evening feeling totally exhausted? Are those days the ones when you have a hard time keeping your spontaneous impulses in check? You're more likely to fall off your new diet plan, procrastinate, put off an important task or get distracted. Why does this phenomenon often occur at the end of the day?

Roy Baumeister and his radishes

The following experiment – conducted by Dr. Roy Baumeister, a renowned social psychologist – may help to shed some light on the question above. The participants were told to fast before the experiment and then spend some time in a room with freshly baked chocolate cookies and raw red radishes. Group 1 was allowed to eat whatever they wanted while group 2 was only allowed to eat the radishes. Immediately afterwards, both groups were told to try and solve a geometric puzzle which was in fact unsolvable. Group 1 gave up after 20 minutes while group 2 threw in the towel after only eight minutes on average – a significant difference. The radish eaters gave up so quickly because their willpower was depleted by resisting the temptation of the cookies. So when they attempted to solve the puzzle, they could no longer find the will to fully engage in another torturous task and that was not simply because some participants were hungrier than others. Further studies were able to prove that the daily repository for our willpower is a limited resource.[20] It is not only depleted by resisting temptations, but also by making decisions. That is why Steve Jobs wore the same polo-neck sweater, why Barack Obama wears the same suit and Mark Zuckerberg the same T-shirt every day – to prevent decision fatigue. Standing in front of your wardrobe in the morning, choosing what clothes to wear or lying in bed deciding whether to hit the snooze button again, can cost a precious amount of energy. And since you dissipate your willpower in the course of your day, you end up with all of it sapped in the evening, leaving you far more prone to indulge yourself in whims, impulses and basic desires. Good habits help prevent this phenomenon from occurring. They require no decision because that has already been taken care of.

“

Motivation is what gets you started.
Habit is what keeps you going.
JIM ROHN

This is why good habits are so incredibly valuable: They help us save willpower

After 500 biceps curls you can barely raise your arm. In much the same way, after facing numerous decisions and temptations, your willpower can no longer deliver peak performance. This is why you're more likely to reach for the tub of Ben & Jerry's or to have a second glass of wine after a particularly hard day at work. For the same reason, excessive studying before a test will lead to some of the worst excesses the night after the test.

For example, why would you want to make healthy decisions throughout the day, over and over again? Why weigh every single small decision separately? Will I have a coke or a glass of water now? Do I opt for a workout session or rather a Netflix session? Do I eat a salad or a cheeseburger? Isn't it a lot easier to establish the habit of eating healthy once, and then be freed of the recurring struggles of making a decision? The same logic applies to every other area of your life: Of course rehearsing a new habit takes a lot of willpower in the beginning, but once this habit has taken root, you can take your hands off the decision-making steering wheel and ease your foot off the willpower accelerator. Now you are free to run on habit cruise control and perform the desired actions on autopilot. Life becomes simpler and many daily struggles and hassles vanish this way. **The things that took so much strength and effort only a while ago are now a breeze**.

If you use *The 6-Minute Diary* regularly, an optimistic attitude becomes one of your new habits. This new habit keeps you from having to waste precious willpower on consciously trying to see things through a more optimistic lens. You're already doing this as a habit. Rituals and automatic responses make life easier because they don't burden your brain unnecessarily. The fewer small decisions you have to take in the course of your day, the more effectively you will make the important ones. This leaves sufficient time and brain capacity for when you need it most, namely to deal with the difficult, significant and urgent matters of your day.

Science confirms: establishing a habit takes 66 days

Psychologist Dr. Phillippa Lally developed an experiment to find out how long it takes to establish and cement new habits. The study was conducted with just under 100 people with an average age of 27. The participants were told to adopt a healthy routine and follow it for 84 consecutive days. They could choose between taking a daily 15-minute walk, eating a fruit with lunch every day or doing 50 sit-ups every morning. It was shown that the period between the conscious execution of the exercise and the automated habit was an average of 66 days.[21] With complex habits, this process takes slightly longer than with simpler ones. In the context of the experiment, eating a piece of fruit with lunch every day was deemed a simple habit while doing 50 sit-ups every morning was a more complex one. Even those who missed a day or two reached their goal in the end. That means you can finish your house of happiness with the help of *The 6-Minute Diary* even if you miss laying a brick for a day or two. To put it in a nutshell:

1. After approximately 66 days, a new behaviour becomes automatic; it becomes part of your life.
2. Building habits is not an all-or-nothing process: Sporadic slips are forgivable.

What makes *The 6-Minute Diary* so special is the fact that each paragraph in the Morning and Evening Routine automatically results in the development of a new, advantageous habit, which then becomes a part of you in a period of approximately 66 days. Every morning and every evening for the next six months, you're spinning a few new threads, cocooning your life in a web of positive habits.

Watch your thoughts, they become words.
Watch your words, they become actions.
Watch your actions, they become habits.
Watch your habits, they become character.
LAO TZU

You can train your willpower just like you can train your biceps

What happens in these 66 days? – In your brain, the prefrontal cortex is responsible for self-control, so this is where your willpower resides. Just like a muscle, it tires with heavy use. While muscles become exhausted by exercise in the short term, they are strengthened by regular exercise in the long term. Similarly, you can improve your willpower to a certain extent and build it up like a muscle. If there is increased activity in one area of the brain, this leads to growth and restructuring of your neuronal pathways. The area actually gets physically larger.[22] What is known as muscle growth or hypertrophy from working out or lifting weights is called neuroplasticity in the central nervous system (brain and spinal cord). If you want to eat two pieces of fruit every morning or establish a practice of meditation, your neuronal pathways will have been reprogrammed to do so after approximately 66 days – through neuroplasticity. The "installation" in your brain is completed, and for the time being can't be reversed so easily. The same goes for a positive attitude or a growth mindset. To attain them, you can rewire your brain by analogue means.

The effect of compound interest

When Albert Einstein was asked what the most powerful force in the universe was, his spontaneous answer was: "The power of compound interest." Warren Buffet, probably the most successful investor of all time, gave the same response when asked about the most important factor of his success. As these gentlemen are two fairly credible sources, they must have a point: If you invest £10,000 with a starting annual interest rate of 5%, you have £10,500 at the end of the first year, but almost £27,000 after twenty years. We're all familiar with the compound interest effect and its significance for our savings account, but you can also benefit from the same effect without investing any money: If you improve by 1% every day, compounded daily, that adds up to 3778% a year – meaning that you are 38 times better than you were when you started. The same growth effects can be seen with human habits. Interest here equals the small steps we take every single day. Proportional to time, the results of these small steps will grow exponentially. It's not the few decisions of galactic proportion that make us happy and successful, but the many accumulated small ones.

> *Small, Smart Choices + Consistency + Time =*
> *RADICAL DIFFERENCE*
> DARREN HARDY

Let me give you a practical example: If you spend ten minutes every day reading about the subject of "personal development", in the short term that doesn't make a big difference in your life. After a month, however, it will begin to give you significant ideas and insights. For instance, one insight might be that you want to integrate more gratitude and appreciation into your life. Another month later, during your daily ten minutes, you stumble upon *The 6-Minute Diary*. You decide to buy it, convinced that from now on, your daily time spent on "personal development" will be well-spent with this book – you will even save four minutes every day. :) You start being more grateful and notice some small, seemingly inconsequential positive changes. Three months later, more gratitude and mindfulness have become an entrenched part of your life and therefore in the long run, you have better relationships, more life satisfaction and you go through your day with more optimism. Your sleep has improved, you handle the strains in your life better and you lead a longer and more fulfilled life. **In the beginning, the effects are fractional, but given time, they become radical!**

> **"**
> *Practice yourself, for heaven's sake in little*
> *things, and then proceed to greater.*
> EPICTETUS

One good habit quickly turns into several

Another parallel between compound interest and habits: Once you have taken the first step, the next ones often follow by themselves. Once you have implemented a good habit, it often acts as the soil from which other good habits grow almost automatically – just like the compound interest in the bank which works on its own once the money has been invested or deposited. To continue the financial analogy, one might say that different habits have lower or higher interest rates. Thus, the establishment of some habits is a far better initial investment of your energy, discipline and willpower than others. Such high-interest habits are also referred to as "keystone habits"[23] and uncontroversial examples are exercise, meditation, reading or writing. Once acquired, keystone habits will find their way into other areas of your life, making other desirable habits more natural and less tedious. Why would you spend your time changing dozens of habits if you can reach your goals by changing only a few? Use your energy intelligently and focus on developing such habits first because they will change, remove and reshape other habits. By using this Diary, you are applying this very strategy as you are ingraining a crucial keystone habit. *The 6-Minute Diary* will increase the richness of your life exponentially, because it leads to the development of multiple good habits such as optimism, daily gratitude and growth through reflection.

> *Compound interest is the eighth wonder of the world.*
> *He who understands it, earns it..., he who doesn't... pays it.*
> ALBERT EINSTEIN

Several studies provide evidence for the effectiveness of keystone habits. For instance, in one of them, the participants had to lift weights for two months. One positive habit triggered others and soon the participants started to eat healthier, reduced their alcohol and cigarette consumption, studied more for their courses and even tidied up their rooms more frequently.[24] In another study, the participants had to keep detailed logs of everything they bought for four months. Again, not only their finances improved, but one habit spilled over into others: they ate healthier, drank less alcohol and caffeine, smoked less, exercised more and were more productive at work.[25] Does that sound familiar? When was the last time you adopted a positive habit? Didn't you notice that other positive habits followed almost automatically?

The bottom line

Habits are the best way to make achieving your goals inevitable. Use *The 6-Minute Diary* every day and watch the magic happen. There is no elevator to take you to your personal success. You have to use the stairs.

Fundamentals 3: Self-Reflection

... where you see yourself and what makes you happy.

What do all parts of the Morning and Evening Routine have in common? Exactly, they increase your happiness step by step if used correctly. To make this possible in the first place, each part of the daily routine initiates highly valuable reflection processes.

What is a reflection process?

Reflecting is an activity where past, present and future actions are being linked in your thoughts. What is crucial here is not what you think, but how you think. In other words, it's the thought process that counts (consider this primarily for *The 5 Weekly Questions* and the Evening Routine). In this process, you assess your actions within the context of past experiences or goals that you've set. It's this assessment that enables you to come up with options and decisions about how you want to proceed.[26] Imagine self-reflection as a lift, which takes you down to your subconscious mind where you can have a closer look at the control centre. Here, you can take your time to gather exclusive insights and examine all the mechanisms and patterns that govern your actions, the way you feel and the way you think. As a result of that process, you're learning new things about yourself and are creating an ideal decision-making tool for any intended behavioural change.

What does science say about this?

It says that people who have a sophisticated ability to self-reflect have advantages in pretty much all areas of life. They are better planners and have a superior way of handling their emotions, they are more disciplined and focused, they make more deliberate decisions and last but not least, they are better at anticipating potential problems.[27]

> ❝
> *You cannot teach a man anything, you can only help him find it within himself.*
>
> GALILEO GALILEI

Self-Reflection as a prerequisite for personal development

How do you want to improve yourself and increase your life satisfaction if you don't even understand yourself? The better you know yourself and the more open your internal dialogue is, the better paved is the road in front of you. Since continuous change is inevitable for long-term happiness, you should avoid getting stuck in your own perspective and in old thinking patterns. Adopting a helicopter view of your own actions is very helpful here because it helps to promote more open dialogues with yourself. Your emotions often act as a sort of straitjacket trying to fight any change, steering you in a particular direction without you even being aware of it. This is where conscious self-reflection comes into play and can act as a starting point to any kind of change. It allows you to observe your emotions instead of being absorbed by them, to identify them instead of identifying with them. It is a means to distance yourself from the whirlwind of your thoughts and the chaotic mess of your emotions. In doing so, you free your actual behaviour from the spontaneity and arbitrariness of your emotions. The more you practise it, the easier you will find it. The daily Evening Routine, *The 5 Weekly Questions* and the occasional glimpse at your past Diary entries will support you in becoming better at supervising your own control centre.

Precious minutes for even more precious questions

What are you thankful for and what is it that makes you happy? How can you incorporate more of that into your life? Haven't you ever experienced how such things become clear when you think about them in moments of calmness and serenity? In the hustle and bustle of everyday life, your brain is so bombarded with external stimuli that it is nearly impossible to distinguish between what is actually your own thought and what is a reaction to your environment. This is exactly the reason why you should use the Diary right after getting up and right before going to bed. At those times, there is no one to disturb you and there are no external factors to influence you. It's just You and Your self-reflection.

VISA – No reflection, no success

If someone reaches for his credit card – anywhere in the world – it is very likely to be a VISA card. Everyone knows VISA but who knows Dee Ward Hock, the man who founded VISA in 1968? For decades he has been the CEO of VISA and is considered a pioneer of the business world. After dealing with management issues for over 50 years, he firmly believes that self-reflection is the key to success. In his view, 50% of one's time should be invested in self-management in order to better understand goals, motives and values as well as one's own behaviour.

Self-Reflection as a continuous process

A man is never the same for long. He is continually changing.
He seldom remains the same even for half an hour.
GEORGE GURDJIEFF

You don't just wake up one day and notice fundamental changes in you. Like the sand on a beach, which slowly and continuously transforms into new shapes and structures, your identity gradually shifts and alters. For this reason, the answers to the important questions of life have to be readdressed and reflected upon again and again. Let's take pension as an example. Who is interested in pension at the age of fifteen? Probably very few people. The picture looks very different about 10 to 15 years later, though, when financial security becomes more important and can contribute remarkably to your overall life satisfaction. When you're a teenager, the things that make you happy are very different from the things that make you happy ten years later. For the same reason, it is often months, years or even decades later that we notice changes in ourselves. The better you follow and understand the change you're continuously undergoing, the better your inner compass for decision-making will become. A sound self-reflection process doesn't take place overnight, and it's not a one-off matter either. Much more, it is an on-going process, a perpetual conversation with yourself. And as with any conversation, the differences in quality can be tremendous. If you're answering a question like "What are you grateful for?" on a superficial level and only once every now and then, the answers will hardly have long lasting effects. The book you're holding in your hands is the chance to answer these questions on a regular basis. Go deeper into yourself and practise valuable self-reflection with minimum expenditure of time.

But I already know what I want...

You're probably convinced that you know it already: a great family, more money, good food, independence, (more) sex, power, fun, variety, holiday and the like. Surely, on a pretty abstract level, you know what you want, but let's get down to the real substance of of what it is that you really want and that makes life meaningful to you. Which very concrete day-to-day activities make you happy? Which small specific actions do you perform on a daily basis to bring you closer to a more fulfilling life? The small actions you carry out are worth far more than the big ones that you plan. With the help of *The 6-Minute Diary*, you will reveal these concrete activities over time. By writing them down regularly, your subconscious mind will remember them and carry them along wherever you are (see RAS, p.52). The more often you do this, the more self-evidently and naturally these concrete actions will become part of Your daily routine and part of You.

The question "What exactly do you want?" becomes increasingly important…

Old jobs vanish and new jobs emerge. Old knowledge loses value and new skills are in demand. Thanks to the Internet, everyone has access to knowledge nowadays, which is why today lifelong learning is more important than ever. We used to praise the loyal employee who stayed with one company all his life. Today, the one-job-for-life concept is a rarity. People used to stay in one place their entire lives, whereas these days, geographical flexibility is almost a must-have requirement. Most of our parents are still doing the jobs they took up after finishing school or they did it until they retired. Nowadays, it seems many people change their jobs more often than their underwear. Changing the study programme, the professional direction or the company has become part of the standard. The overwhelming variety of career options makes it increasingly harder to follow a single path and to stick to it. This abundance of choice can be applied to all other decisions in life. There are countless books on one and the same topic, countless products, which serve one and the same purpose, and countless service providers with one and the same service. We are presented with more and more options while given less and less time. We're missing the wood for the trees.

Due to the almost infinite number of options and life paths, it is all the more important to ask yourself what it is that you want in the first place. This is the first step to focus on what exactly fulfills you most. Decades of research show that we are very inaccurate judges of what made us happy in the past. When remembering what made us happy, we tend to add and remove key details without realising it, although very often, these details might have been the ones which made us happy.[28] **By using The 6-Minute Diary, you prevent falling victim to imprecise memories which in turn gives you a better chance of reproducing the mosaic of your happiness.** Obviously you won't gain such insights after three Diary entries but clarity will come in the course of time.

What better way is there to remember what you really want other than writing it down every day? What are you looking forward to, what are you grateful for and which events fulfilled your day? By answering these questions daily, you set the right mental processes in motion again and again. The 6-Minute Diary is a little key that can open very huge doors for you. It can help you open the door to find out what exactly makes you happy in life. It is You who has to walk through the door, though.

>
> ## If a man knows not to which port he sails, no wind is favorable.
>
> LUCIUS ANNAEUS SENECA

The
Morning Routine
... and why it is the perfect start for your day.

When you arise in the morning, think of what a privilege
it is to be alive – to breathe, to think, to enjoy, to love.
MARCUS AURELIUS

The way you start your morning often defines what kind of day you are going to have. The Morning Routine in *The 6-Minute Diary* is aimed at releasing dopamine and making sure you're fully awake. That way you can use the first moments of your day to charge your batteries with positive energy and to start a productive day. It's like taking aim with bow and arrow: You concentrate on the day ahead, draw the bow and get ready to attack your targets for the rest of the day. No matter at what time you get up, the Morning Routine is the most essential routine of them all. Try to find a successful person who doesn't have a fixed morning ritual; it's like looking for a needle in a haystack. But maybe you've never been a real morning person or you think you don't have a few minutes before you leave the house? In that case, please read about the following morning routines of people who are all a lot busier than ordinary mortals like us.

Nobody is too busy to spare the time
to tell everyone how busy he is.
ROBERT LEMBKE

Barack Obama: The former President of the United States strictly starts his morning routine two hours before his first official appointment of the day. In these two hours, he doesn't allow any media or news to influence his brain. Six times a week, he spends 45 minutes doing cardio and weightlifting, and after the exercise he has breakfast with his family. He says about his mornings: "When I follow my morning routine, the rest of my day is a lot more productive."

Arianna Huffington: Due to her great influence, the editor-in-chief of the online newspaper *HuffPost* is often heralded as "Queen of the bloggers." Her day begins with breathing exercises, 30 minutes of meditation, and writing down three things she's grateful for. Following that, she takes her morning coffee and defines her goals for the day. She is so convinced of the positive effects meditation has on her life that she offers weekly meditation courses to her staff, free of charge. During her morning routine, she avoids glancing at her phone for as long as possible.

Jack Dorsey: He is the inventor and co-founder of both, Twitter and Square. As CEO of two billion-dollar corporations he works 16 hours a day, eight for Square and eight for Twitter. And yet, he manages to set aside time every single morning by getting up at 5:30 to meditate for 30 minutes and then either runs ten kilometres or exercises for another 30 minutes. [If you enjoyed reading these morning routines, allow yourself to read 25 more of them in our e-Book "The Golden Morning Routine", which you can find on createurbestself.com/stayontheball]

The list may be extended indefinitely: Bill Gates, Maya Angelou, Richard Branson, Woody Allen, Cameron Diaz, Stephen King, Michelle Obama, Sir Alan Sugar, Hillary Clinton, Sylvester Stallone, Tim Ferriss, Arnold Schwarzenegger, Melinda Gates, Kate Middleton... they all have morning rituals they follow. And bear in mind this isn't a 21st century phenomenon: Marcus Aurelius, Ludwig van Beethoven, Johann Wolfgang von Goethe, Winston Churchill, Ernest Hemingway, Sigmund Freud, Agatha Christie, Charles Darwin, Mark Twain, William Shakespeare, Immanuel Kant, Jane Austen, and a lot of other people we remember knew the value of a morning routine long before our time. They all had or have fixed morning rituals, and all made or make time for themselves first thing in the morning. Do you still think you can't invest three minutes in your own well-being in the morning?

Set aside some time for yourself in the morning

"In the event of emergency, secure your own oxygen mask before helping others." There is a good reason behind this safety instruction: If you cannot breathe you can't help others either. The same thing can be applied to everyday life: Once you have left the house in the morning, your energy is mostly spent on duties in the service of others. During the day, you set your own needs aside more often than you think. So it makes even more sense to take care of your own needs before that. This way, you fully charge your batteries for the day instead of already sapping the energy supply in the morning. And this is anything but selfish because remember that as soon as you can breathe you can help others to do so, too. So the next time you feel "too tired" or you woke up "too late", write in your *6-Minute Diary* anyway. Put yourself at the top of your priority list and commit to carving those few extra minutes into your morning schedule.

> **Your first duty is to make yourself happy.**
> **It is only when you are happy that you**
> **can make others happy, too.**
> LUDWIG ANDREAS FEUERBACH

Do you act or react?

Either you run the day or the day will run you. A reactive person says "I have to", "I have no time for that," "I can't," or "Why is it always me having such a hard time?" The proactive person on the other hand will say: "I want," "I'll make time for that," "I'll find out how to do it," or, "What can I do to be happier?". To begin the day proactively means to start it in a creative, formative and self-determined manner.

The major part of the population starts their day reactively. 78% of the people who own a mobile phone check their phones within the first 15 minutes after getting up.[29] Their first glance is predominantly directed at services like Facebook, Instagram or WhatsApp, and their email inbox. To avoid distorting your own thoughts with other people's lives early in the morning, you should try to avoid such reactive activities. Start your morning by focusing on yourself first. Doing so will help you to focus better on everything else for the rest of the day.

No matter how busy they are, most successful people don't begin their day with reactive activities. They don't answer emails first; they don't immediately check their phones to reply to messages. Instead, they start their day proactively and you can do this too by changing the first thing you do in the morning. Make opening your *6-Minute Diary* a routine in the morning and secure your first-class ticket into proactive territory. After all, you reap what you sow – only in this case you'll even be able to see your harvest on that same day.

Women in Japan

Japanese women have the highest life expectancy worldwide, namely 87 years.[30] Let's be optimistic and assume you'll live to at least the age of 87, too. Accordingly, your adult life (18 to 87) amounts to more than 25,000 days.

So you get up more than 25,000 times in your adult life! How many of these mornings have passed by you unconsciously? Think of the immense effect that a meaningful morning routine could have had. Use your imagination and picture this effect for a moment...

Holding *The 6-Minute Diary* in your hands, you already have a fundamental pillar of your morning routine. Open it and you will get up on the right side of bed every morning. To paraphrase a quote by Aurelius Augustinus: In the first morning hour you should be at the helm, for this is the time you set the course for the day.

❶ Your gratitude

Gratitude is not only the greatest of virtues,
but the parent of all the others.
MARCUS TULLIUS CICERO

The immense importance of gratitude is one of the few topics on this planet that atheists, believers of all world religions and scientists agree on. The grateful person is able to fully enjoy positive feelings and to experience negative feelings – such as anger, guilt, grief or envy – to a lesser extent in the long run. The grateful person has a stronger sense of self-worth and is better equipped to handle stresses and strains of everyday life. Gratitude makes you sleep better[31] and live longer[32]. If you are grateful, you are more cooperative and thus strengthen your relationships with other people. The grateful person finds it easier to establish and maintain fulfilling personal relationships.

Interestingly, you don't necessarily have to express your gratitude with words to reap those benefits. Studies – like the one by Dr. Seligman described on the following page – show that merely writing down what you are grateful for has substantial effects on your well-being. Also, it doesn't matter whether you're extremely or only a little bit grateful. What is of primary importance for the effect on your happiness is that you feel some form of gratitude at all on a regular basis. It takes practice and effort to make this a habit. But once you've established this, and gratitude has become your attitude, the positive cycle of gratitude is initiated, gradually but inexorably it will start spreading its benefits into your life. Simply use this book to practise the most important skill of happiness: daily gratitude.

Oprah Winfrey on her gratitude diary

Oprah Winfrey, one of the most influential and popular women in the world, used to be the host of one of the most successful American talk shows of all time: The Oprah Winfrey Show. Every morning since 1996, she has been writing down five things she is grateful for right after getting up. In 2012, she commented on her decision to keep a gratitude diary: "I will have to say, it was the single most important thing – I believe – I've ever done." She also emphasises the significance of gratitude in general: "No matter what is going on in your life, I believe if you concentrate on what you have, you'll always end up having more [...]. If you focus on what you don't have, you will never, ever, ever have enough."[33]

More evidence for the beneficial effects of *The 6-Minute Diary*

*Gratitude is the healthiest of all human emotions. The more
you express gratitude for what you have, the more likely
you will have even more to express gratitude for.*

ZIG ZIGLAR

Dr. Martin Seligman is the founder of Positive Psychology. His research on the maximisation of personal happiness and life satisfaction has been recognised among experts for decades. In one of his best-known studies, almost 600 participants adopted one of five different activities geared at maximising happiness. The only two successful activities were:[34]

1. Writing down great things that happened in the course of their day; this is equivalent to what you will do every day as the last part of the Evening Routine in your *6-Minute Diary*.
2. Expressing gratitude in the form of a letter of gratitude; this is what you do in a slightly different form in the Morning Routine.

In particular, the effects of the gratitude exercise were stunning and have been replicated in other studies since. After one week, the participants were measurably happier than before. But here's the kicker: Follow-up tests which were conducted a week, a month, three months and six months later showed that each time the participants were still happier than they were before they took the initial test. One week of daily practice was enough for all the participants of the study to feel measurably happier even six months afterwards. If the long-term effect is already this significant after only one week, you can certainly imagine what effect daily gratitude can have for you over a longer period of time. If gratitude were available as a pill, it would probably be the best selling drug of all time. Until that pill is invented, the book in your hands is a good place to start.

"

*It is not the happy people who are grateful.
It is the grateful people who are happy.*

FRANCIS BACON

Gratitude gears the focus towards the good in life

In every exalted joy, there mingles a sense of gratitude.
MARIE VON EBNER-ESCHENBACH

Making gratitude an integral part of your life automatically triggers an optimistic outlook on life – in short: gratitude and a healthy optimism go hand in hand. The more optimistic you are, the more there will be to be grateful for. Or as Plato already put it 2,500 years ago: "A grateful mind is a great mind which eventually attracts to itself great things." How often do you think about the daily gifts your life offers you? How often do you think about all the beautiful small things you encounter? And, how often are small irrelevant issues bothering you?

In our fast-paced modern world where there is constant pressure to perform, we often don't find the time for gratitude and appreciation. The queue at the post office, the new posts on Facebook, the argument with your family, your endless to-do-list and news on supposed terror attacks, wars or natural disasters gear our attention towards the negative rather than the positive. **If you don't proactively gear your attention towards the positive, the negative will continuously flood your perception.** The natural tendency of your survival software to overemphasise the negative is also anything but helping here.

If you are consciously practicing gratitude, you direct your perception towards the things that make you happy and the things that you enjoy. This isn't to say you should lower your expectations and be satisfied 24/7. Rather it means that being grateful will ultimately foster your success, not the other way around. The happiness resulting from gratitude fosters achievement, not the other way around.[35]

I've failed over and over and over again
in my life. And that is why I succeed.
MICHAEL JORDAN

Likewise, the failure to fulfil your expectations is not opposed to happiness. Quite the contrary: The ability to stumble and fall – to not fulfil your own expectations – and to still appreciate the experience itself, is a fundamental element of personal fulfilment. An attitude that considers every failure as temporary and as a door opener for new opportunities is an integral part of gratitude and happiness. There is no progress without failure and progress is what drives your happiness. This is why embracing the inevitable failures of life is so essential. Dale Carnegie, one of the most successful writers of all time, described the difference between positive and negative thinking as early as 1948: "Positive thinking deals with causes and effects and leads to logical, constructive planning; bad thinking frequently leads to tension and nervous breakdowns."[36] When you adopt a positive outlook on your own life, you create the ideal basis for lifelong personal development. Research shows that people who have a healthy portion of optimism live 20% longer, are physically healthier, more successful in their jobs and have more satisfying relationships.[37] Those who know how to apply the concept of gratitude automatically shift their focus towards the positive things, and are thus a crucial step ahead of 99% of the Western world today. Gratitude is not old-fashioned at all, if anything, it is highly modern!

Tony Robbins on his "Highway to Happiness"

The most successful performance and personality coach in the world had clients such as Bill Clinton, Serena Williams and Andre Agassi. He still sells millions of books and holds sold-out seminars. For years, he has been taking three and a half minutes every single morning to write down and also feel gratitude for three things in his life. In this regard, he says: "The reason for gratitude is: The two emotions that mess us up the most are fear and anger. And you can't be grateful and fearful simultaneously, they don't go together. And you can't be angry and grateful simultaneously." To Robbins, gratitude is unique because it overpowers negative emotions. That's why he calls this part of his morning routine the "highway to happiness."[38]

You transfer your gratitude to others. They transfer it back to you in return

Happiness is a perfume you cannot pour
on others without getting some on yourself.
RALPH WALDO EMERSON

The psychologist Bernard Weiner defines gratitude as a two-stage cognitive process. First, you experience a positive moment and then you realise that an external source (God, nature, another person) is responsible for this event. According to Weiner, gratitude is therefore always directed towards an external source in some way. Often the gratitude you will express in *The 6-Minute Diary* will be directed towards other people and that is the point where the magical spiral of gratitude begins: As you internalise your gratitude this way, your behaviour towards these people will start reflecting that. Even without consciously deciding to do so, you will naturally be and come across as a nicer and more genuine person. For this reason, your friends and colleagues will naturally be nicer to you, and that in turn, will make you happier – the positive vibes you radiate will come back to you. And by reflecting on your little good deeds every day (Evening Routine), you engender a similar upward spiral. Writing in your *6-Minute Diary* thus equals initiating a wonderfully positive cycle that will strengthen your personal relationships.

Gratitude – The glue that binds people together

Dr. Philip C. Watkins wrote a book entitled "Gratitude and the Good Life." Looking at a multitude of studies and analyses, he comes to the conclusion that gratitude is one of the most important components of a happy life. With regard to the social environment and the significance of gratitude for personal relationships, he draws the following conclusions:[39]

1. Being grateful makes you more likable and pleasant to be around.
2. Gratitude helps you in building and maintaining relationships in a very unique way.
3. Gratitude fosters prosocial behaviour in yourself and your environment.

What is prosocial behaviour? – In general, it encompasses all behaviour that is aimed at the well-being of others, intentionally or unintentionally. Forms of prosocial behaviour include helping, cooperating, sharing, supporting, praising, but also politeness, compassion or empathy for others. So when you ask yourself in the Evening Routine what you did for other people, you reflect on your prosocial behaviour.

> *A person's real wealth*
> *is the wealth of his real relationships.*
> KARL MARX

Human beings are social beings by nature. That's why it is no surprise that social ties and relationships are crucial for our life satisfaction. And as with most things in life, it is more about quality than quantity. Focusing on the quality of your relationships leads to more meaningful and satisfying relationships. Dr. Seligman and Dr. Diener conducted several studies to find out what distinguishes particularly happy people – namely, the top 10% – from the remaining 90%. The outstanding feature was their close relationships with family and friends, with whom they spent a lot of time on a regular basis. Again, these studies showed that the perceived quality and depth of those interpersonal relationships was the crucial factor.[40] Genuine appreciation is one of the best tools to build such close relationships and probably the most effective booster shot for relationship maintenance.

"

Happiness is the only thing that multiplies when you share it.

ALBERT SCHWEITZER

❷ This is how I'll make today great

A trivial but crucial little anecdote

A man meets three workers at a construction site.
He asks the first one: "What are you doing here?" – "I'm laying bricks."
Then he asks the second one: "What are you doing here?" – "I'm building a wall."
Finally, he approaches the third worker and asks him the same question. The worker looks up with a smile on his face and replies: "I'm building a church."

What is this little anecdote supposed to tell us? If you want to be a man or woman of action, always keep in mind three things: First, you need to envision "the church" to have the right attitude towards your goals. Second, you need to decide which walls you want to build. This means you need to be clear about your smaller goals and priorities. And third, you need to lay the bricks that are necessary to build the wall. This is exactly what you do in this section. You focus on your walls and write down which bricks you need to lay – which small actions are essential to get there. In the end, it's these little decisions that shape your life.

From anecdote to Diary

Okay, it all makes sense, but how exactly do I apply this to *The 6-Minute Diary*? – To help you put these ideas about walls and bricks into action, you can use structures such as this one:

I will do (small action/lay a brick) because I want to feel _____.

1. I will set aside ten minutes to continue my new book because I'm excited about what happens next.
2. Today I will eat three pieces of fruit because I want to feel healthy.
3. I will go to the gym because I want to feel attractive and balanced.
4. Tonight I will go to the party because I want to feel sociable and have fun.
5. I will sit straight during the meeting because I want to feel confident.

The "because" part forces you to pay attention to the motivational drivers behind the goals you are setting. You are taking those few extra seconds to check if your goals really resonate with your personality and are a true reflection of what you want. You write down which bricks you need to lay in order to build your wall(s). Your actions don't have to be massive at all. The main thing is to keep them small enough so you will actually execute them. If you keep executing your small actions over a longer period of time, you'll see your own finished "church" sooner than you imagined.

How to tempt fate and make your own luck

Chance only favors the prepared mind.
LOUIS PASTEUR

There are some things – such as nice weather, winning the lottery, high-speed Wi-Fi or phased traffic lights – that you cannot control or plan. Even though sunshine would make your day lovely, you cannot conjure it up. This is why you do not ask WHAT would make today great, but HOW you'll make today great in this part of the Diary. The focus lies on concrete actions that are within your sphere of influence. Some things – such as close friendships or a date with your soul mate – are also difficult to control or plan, but still a lot easier than the weather or the lottery draw. You can always focus your attention on doing small things that increase the probability of accidental great results. In this way, you initiate a cycle of nice occurrences, a virtuous cycle. This is how it can work:

1. Focus your attention on smiling more often → More people around you will return your smile → More people will be kind and friendly → More friendships will be formed "by accident".

   For instance, start by giving the barista a smile when you get your coffee in the morning. It might feel odd to begin with, but the more you practise it, the more genuine your smile will become and the more natural it will come across.

2. Focus your attention on your posture → You will be more attractive in the eyes of the opposite sex, because a good posture is sexy[41] → More "coincidental" dating opportunities will arise.

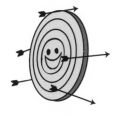  

In the beginning   After a while   After a longer period of time

As you can see you CAN actually tempt fate. Of course a process like this is not linear, but in the long run, the point is: the more small acts you perform towards the direction of your goal, the higher is the probability of "accidental" good things that will happen to you. The way this chain reaction works is based on the effect of compound interest, which was described earlier (p.35). Success compounds success. Once small successes have been achieved, they multiply automatically and exponentially.

A simple recipe: Once you start to cook, the food will be tasty anyway

The brain processes more than 400 million bits of information per second, but only 2000 of those penetrate your consciousness.[42] 99,9995% of the information remains unnoticed. Your brain's Reticular Activating System (RAS) extracts only those things that are important to you. By asking yourself how you'll make the day ahead great, you've already put one foot on the home straight. Let's assume you'd write: "I will eat healthy food with lots of fruit and vegetables." The anticipation and visualisation of this intention are processed in your RAS – the filter of your reality. [43] Your perception automatically focuses on all opportunities that you connect to your intention, meaning that your search radar is sensitised for all targets in its search radius. In this case, you've calibrated your radar to be geared towards healthy meals, fruit and vegetables. You simply capitalised on the RAS' ability to bring more good into your life.

Hocus-pocus? Well, go ahead and try it. What was the last thing you bought and have been using a lot? Maybe a pair of shoes? Since you bought them, haven't you noticed that there are lots of other people wearing the same or a similar pair of shoes? You buy a certain type of car, or someone you know does, and now you see the very same model all the time? You're pregnant and start seeing pregnant women everywhere? You start exercising and suddenly everyone around you looks like they're working out, too? Or let's take an even more obvious example: You're at a cocktail party and because of the hubbub of voices, all you can hear is general noise. And yet, as soon as your name is mentioned somewhere, your ears will stick out like those of Dumbo. This selective perception is governed by the RAS and the beautiful thing is that the Morning Routine stimulates your RAS to deal more with the things that make you happy. This will eventually help you achieve your daily goals, because a happy brain works approximately 30% more productively and creatively than a brain in a neutral or negative state.[44] When you use *The 6-Minute Diary* in the morning, you have set your filter for the day ahead of you – a filter that will make your day better. Start making every day a great day!

❸ Positive Affirmation

This part of the Morning Routine is not as self-explanatory as the others. Since 95% of your decision-making has its origin in the subconscious mind,[45] the beliefs and thoughts on the subconscious level have an immense impact on your reality (see p.55). With the help of positive affirmations, you can put unconscious brain mechanisms in the driver's seat: let them remove subconscious obstacles and help you push your limits to create the reality you want. Brain-imaging studies that examined the neural mechanisms associated with affirmations have shown the effectiveness of this technique.[46] If used correctly, affirmations are a proven method to prime your brain and create gradual change from within. They can raise the level of feel-good hormones and push your brain to activate neural pathways for positive and optimistic thinking. Your subconscious mind is a relentless workaholic, active both day and night. **By using _The 6-Minute Diary_ consistently, you put this subconscious workaholic into action and take full advantage of its extraordinary abilities.** You can choose between two different approaches for your daily affirmations: The Jackhammer Approach or the Hummingbird Approach. Choose the one you like most and stick with it for the time being.

Whatever we plant in our subconscious mind and nourish with repetition and emotion will one day become a reality.

EARL NIGHTINGALE

1. Jackhammer Approach: You pick a positive affirmation that you really want to integrate into your life and write it down every day. The more often you do this, the more you internalise the belief in it. You virtually "hammer home" this positive affirmation into your subconscious mind until you consciously experience its benefits and it becomes part of your life. For example: "I love myself which is why I do a job that really fulfills me" or "I trust my inner compass and believe that it will guide me in the right direction" You can also be more specific: "I make £3,000 a month", "I lose weight every day until I reach my ideal weight of 145 pounds" or: "I respect and appreciate my partner and have a loving and passionate relationship."

"

Whether you think you can, or you think you can't – you're right.

HENRY FORD

Jim Carrey's Jackhammer Approach

Jim Carrey went so far as to write himself a £10 million check for "acting services rendered" which he post-dated 10 years and kept in his wallet. He also wrote down every day: "Everybody wants to work with me. I'm a really good actor. I have all kinds of great movie offers." At the time, Carrey was jobless and had never made a penny with his acting. He kept looking at his check and kept it in his wallet until years later, when he actually made that amount of money with an acting job. This is by no means a unique case. The method has proven extremely effective for many other successful people, among them: Muhammad Ali, Bruce Lee, Napoleon Hill, Arnold Schwarzenegger, Oprah Winfrey, Tim Ferriss, Louise Hay, Tony Robbins, Lady Gaga, Tiger Woods and Will Smith.

2. Hummingbird Approach: Here, your affirmation depends on your current feeling or your plans for the day. This means that you determine what it will be every day anew. For example, if you have to deliver a presentation you can write: "I'm competent and eloquent and will show this to my audience by delivering a great speech." If you're currently working on a new project, you can write: "I consider every problem that will arise at work as an opportunity in disguise."

Your subconscious mind does not speak in words, but in emotions. For this reason, the quality indicator of your affirmation is what you're feeling as you write it down. Ask yourself the right questions to find out if you actually feel what you write here:

a) Do you feel worse? – Your subconscious mind probably doesn't believe in your affirmation. You've probably decided to do more than you can realistically achieve.

b) Do you believe what you just wrote? Do you feel better and motivated? – If you do, you're on the right track. You've put yourself into the realm of your growth potential.

c) Do you feel neutral? – Then you're probably not thinking big enough.

Here is one example for the Jackhammer Approach: Sofia always loved designing and creating things. She's 35 and works at a start-up that's been selling innovatively designed shoes made from eco-friendly materials for two years. Sofia is among ten other employees within the Design Department and by the end of the year, one of them is supposed to be appointed as Head of Department. These could be the daily affirmations for Sofia who really wants the new role:

a) "I will take over the CEO's role this year, because I love my job and am strongly convinced of my abilities." (upper smiley)

b) "I'm determined to become Head of the Design Department this year, since I'm fully suited to do the job and designing awesome shoes fulfills me."

c) "I'm satisfied with selling beautiful and eco-friendly shoes to people and I'll see how things develop."

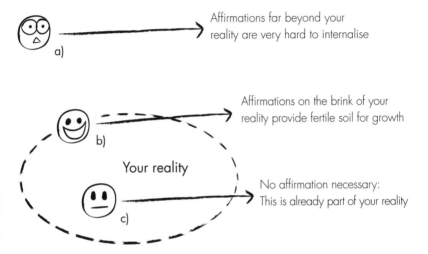

a) Affirmations far beyond your reality are very hard to internalise

b) Affirmations on the brink of your reality provide fertile soil for growth

Your reality

c) No affirmation necessary: This is already part of your reality

It's important that your affirmation is actually positive. Let's say you write, "I won't eat any more chocolate." What does your brain do with that sentence? It starts thinking about chocolate, because it doesn't think in negations. Or the classic example: No matter what you do, don't think of a pink elephant! Well? What did the elephant you just pictured look like? Probably pretty pink, right? Negative phrasing or negations are out of place here because your subconscious mind can't register them.[47] It's equally important to phrase your affirmation as specifically and personally as possible. General statements such as "I love myself" or "I am confident" are less effective than phrases that are tailored to your individual life, such as: "I'm emotionally stable and stay calm even in stressful situations." It's recommended that you begin your daily affirmations with an active part such as, "I am," "I control," or "I have," since your subconscious is able to process your goals directly if you start your phrases this way.

The
Evening Routine

... this is how you reflect and recharge your batteries for the following day.

There is really nothing like a good night's sleep. Do you know the feeling when you get up in the morning and feel thoroughly refreshed and rejuvenated? If you stick to the Evening Routine, that feeling will become the rule rather than the exception. Once you hit 60, you will have spent about 20 years of your life sleeping. Needless to say, you should give your sleep the attention it deserves. So when you go to bed, negative internal dialogues and uncomfortable thoughts should have no place. As the Evening Routine makes sure your thoughts revolve around how to improve and what went well, it is a good idea to do it in the last minutes of your day. By taking inventory of your small successes, you make sure to fall asleep in a relaxed state and get a good night's rest. *The 6-Minute Diary* serves as the key, which unlocks your day in the morning and locks it again at night.

What do you normally do before you go to sleep? – According to a study about the consumer behaviour of 49,000 mobile phone owners from 30 different countries, 62% of them look at their phones in the last five minutes before they go to sleep.[48] Most probably you're also among those who use some kind of electronic device, whether it's your laptop, tablet, smart phone or TV. A variety of different studies show how unhealthy this is, since both the quality and the quantity of your sleep will be drastically reduced in the long term.[49] The light from electronic devices miscues the brain and promotes wakefulness. Even at a low brightness level your smartphone emits sufficient light to prevent the brain from releasing melatonin, a hormone that tells your body it's night-time.[50] **The 6-Minute Diary is not an electronic device and therefore represents a first step towards optimal sleep and a healthier You.**

> "
> *If you don't honour the night,*
> *you're not worthy of the day.*
> ITALIAN PROVERB

❹ My good deed today

He's only glad who gives away.
JOHANN WOLFGANG VON GOETHE

Doing good deeds for others has a lasting effect on your happiness

As logged in his 1793 biography, Benjamin Franklin asked himself two questions each day: In the morning he asked "What good shall I do today?" and at the end of the day "What good have I done today?". This section has a similar objective, because it is all about becoming more intentional in your ability to help and to do good for others, but also in keeping yourself accountable for your actions on a daily basis. People who like to help others and show a tendency towards prosocial behaviour, evaluate themselves as happier than those who don't.[51] So how happy does it actually make us to do something good for other people? Scientists in the United States conducted an experiment to find out: The participants of the study received £100 each and were free to decide whether they would donate the money to a charity of their choice or spend it for themselves. Brain scans were used to examine the brain activities during the experiment. It turns out, the brain area responsible for joy and pleasure was more active in the donor group than in those who used the money for themselves.[52] The same area is in charge of releasing dopamine, as for example when you engage in human reproductive behaviour or let a delicious piece of chocolate melt in your mouth. Other studies have shown that the sense of pleasure triggered by giving is very different from that experienced through sex or tasty food: The positive effects that giving has on your well-being can last throughout the day or even longer, while they fade much quicker in the latter case.[53]

Character does not reveal itself in great deeds.
It is the small things that betray a man's true nature.
JEAN-JACQUES ROUSSEAU

Of course you don't donate money every day, which is also why you need to pay attention to the small acts of kindness in your day. The favour you did your colleague at work, the small gift you got for your friend, doing your roommate's dishes along with yours, or helping your mother with an application. Ask your grandparents how they are doing. Talk to somebody who seems lonely. Tell your partner you love him or her. Express your gratitude to your friends, family and colleagues. Compliment the cook on the food they put in front of you. Hold the door for someone. Lend a sympathetic ear. Put a smile on your face and say "Good morning" to your neighbour or just give a genuine smile to the cashier at the supermarket.

➎ How I will improve

Success is not the key to happiness.
Happiness is the key to success.
ALBERT SCHWEITZER

Since you're holding this book in your hands, it is safe to assume that you want to learn, grow and evolve. Continuous improvement is like cleaning your flat. As soon as you stop cleaning, dust collects and so the need to clean never ends. This section is about appreciating this continuous journey – rather than just the destination. If the only thing to make you happy were reaching big goals, happiness would be a very rare emotion. It is good to have an end to journey toward, but in the end it is the journey that matters. In other words: The end results don't define us, it's the process that does. The point is to be reminded that only you are in charge of tomorrow and to realise that although you can never be perfect, you can constantly work to improve yourself. And if you find that you just had an amazing day where everything went great, you can simply draw a happy smiley in this field.

The aim of this question is to identify persistent problems and opportunities for improvement, so you can derive concrete actions to address them. Don't bite off more than you can chew. Smaller goals lead to bigger results in the long run. Therefore, keep the intended actions you write down here small and achievable – even laughably small, if necessary. The wording of this section was chosen very carefully: It forces you to think about ways you can make things better, to elicit a positive and traceable response instead of focusing on the negative. You reassure yourself that you're going to do better next time, instead of dwelling on or feeling guilty about what went wrong. Immerse yourself in change, because if nothing changes now, nothing will change in the future.

Do NOT compare yourself TO OTHERS. Compare yourself to the person you were yesterday

In some cases, comparing yourself to other people can be a useful source of motivation. In most cases, however, the drawbacks of this source for motivation outweigh its benefits. 20 years ago, the motto may still have been to "keep up with the Joneses," your neighbours and colleagues. These days, thanks to the Internet and especially social media, we're invited to compare ourselves to more and more people. Just this week, another two 'friends' of yours got married and everyone seems to be on holiday in the most beautiful places on earth. And then there's this other friend who just developed an innovative app. Anyway, everyone is super happy! Although it is clear that everyone tailors and tweaks this representation of their lives for public consumption, we keep falling into the same trap: We compare the private reality of our own lives with the public highlights of other people's lives. **We keep comparing our insides with someone else's outsides.**

> *Everyone sees what you appear to be,*
> *few experience what you really are.*
> NICCOLÒ MACHIAVELLI

Because of constant comparison, we have a hard time distinguishing between behaviour, which is primarily motivated by ourselves and behaviour, which is caused by the influence of others. Do I want to climb up the career ladder because that will really fulfil me, or is it because I believe that I have to achieve something in order to be worth something? Do I want to go to the gym because I genuinely enjoy it, or simply because all my friends do it? Constant comparison chips away at your self-esteem. As a result, you become increasingly prone to depression[54] and experience many other downsides, which most likely you've already gone through in one way or another. Social media has managed to extend the standard of comparison in such a way that today it's more important than ever to become aware of the disadvantages of comparing oneself to others, and to work as consciously as possible to reduce them. Of course this is hard, especially when everyone's life is streaming in front of your eyes. Choosing when you dip into that stream is a good point to start. Give it a try and minimise your social media and digital time for a week. Observe how you feel and draw your own conclusions.

Don't compare yourself to others. Compare yourself TO THE PERSON YOU WERE YESTERDAY

When you use *The 6-Minute Diary*, you're taking a large step in precisely that direction. The Diary is not merely a lovely memento for a few months or years from now, it's also a meaningful reminder of where you stood yesterday or last week, and thus a valuable starting point for short-term comparison with yourself. The daily evening question of how you plan to improve helps you monitor and understand your development while re-reading your Diary entries enables you to easily detect tendencies and patterns. The more frequently you write down the same opportunities for improvement, the more aware you should become of these aspects. If for example you keep writing, "I will work out today," without ever putting the plan into action, you need to change your tactic. You could phrase your plan differently and write: "I will consciously plan my day so I can take an hour off for exercise." The same applies to your daily gratitude. If you find that you haven't expressed your gratitude to your partner for several weeks, you're getting valuable clues, which you might only have noticed months or years later otherwise.

❻ Great things I experienced today

A positive mindset may significantly extend your life

The correlation between a person's positive attitude and his life expectancy has hardly ever been demonstrated as clearly as in the so-called "nun study". 180 nuns took part in this long-term study that spanned over a period of 70 years. To be accepted into the convent, the nuns had to write a short autobiography of two to three pages about their lives and what will lie ahead. When they drafted these documents in the 1930s and 40s, they were 22 years old on average. What was examined in the 180 biographies was the amount of negative, neutral and positive words and sentences. Then the nuns were grouped according to the frequency of occurrence of these words, resulting in four groups of 45 women each. The results were stunning:[55]

1. The 45 happiest nuns lived on average 10 years (!) longer than the 45 unhappiest.
2. At the age of 85, more than 90% (!) of the happiest nuns were still alive.
3. 54% of the happiest nuns lived to at least the age of 94, while in the unhappiest group only 15% reached this age.

What makes those observations so significant? – The conditions of this scientific experiment are priceless, since the nuns lived in virtually identical circumstances or still do: They don't drink alcohol, don't smoke, don't have sex, aren't married, have no children, live in the same building, do similar work and eat the same food. Amongst other things, the study shows that happiness has little to do with what happens to us in our lives, and much more with how we choose to see things. Furthermore, the study highlights the importance of appreciating what you already have in your life, of appreciating what your days have to offer right now. As we highlighted in the beginning of this Diary: **Take the time to celebrate the small moments of happiness in your life. Allow yourself to appreciate and cherish the small successes of your day. If you make happiness a priority, longevity may be a happily welcomed side effect.**

> *Life is to 10% what happens to you and 90% how you react to it.*
> CHARLES SWINDOLL

A good start is pretty smart

We cannot change the wind. But we can adjust the sails.
ARISTOTLE

What is usually the first thing you tell your friends, your partner or your roommate when you see them? When you return from work, you might feel the urge to vent all your pent-up negative energy: you might talk about how exhausting and stressful your day was, what annoyed you or what went wrong, only to get a similar response from your listener: "Oh, my boss never praises me or says thank you and he doesn't understand I only have two hands, and then my mother called and all she did was nag...". The simplest way to turn this tired pattern on its head is to talk about the best thing that happened to you today. Even if it feels strange in the beginning, start the conversation by only talking about the best moments of your day, no matter how small or insignificant they may have seemed. No exception. Talk about what you learned, what you were proud of, about that delicious dessert you had, about a funny moment or about the bus you caught only because it was three minutes behind schedule. This puts both, you and your conversation partner, in a positive mood, and you're primed to notice the amazing things – big and small – which happen to you every day. Imagine how great it would be if your friends or partner did the same. Being able to vent about the problems and downsides of the day may sometimes be relieving and help us work through them, but the way you begin a conversation usually sets the tone for the rest of it. This small pointer can become a fantastic connector in any type of relationship! What do you stand to lose if you try to focus on the upsides first – no matter how small they are?

Create your own good mood stock

Sometimes motivating yourself and facing life's challenges isn't easy. At times life gets you down and you simply don't feel so great. Those are the moments when you need small motivational impulses, which help you focus on the essential and good things. Especially the small wins can easily be forgotten. If you think about it now: Can you remember the best three things that happened to you last week? – Probably not, unless you are keeping track. Luckily, you are documenting your happy moments in this final part of the Evening Routine. Every day, you record what made you happy and thus write your own happiness story. Use these entries as your supply of homemade fortune cookies. Reread what you wrote here when you felt better, and your mood will automatically improve. Incidentally, you've piled up a stock of good-spirit nuggets without expiration date, a stock that you can snack on whenever you feel like it. **The most nourishing wellspring you can draw from is You.**

6 Tips

... to stick with it and to get the most out of the Diary.

Tip 1: Find a fixed place for the Diary

If you want to use *The 6-Minute Diary* consistently, one of the most important decisions will be where you want to keep the Diary and the pen you want to use with it. This may sound trivial, but it's really significant. Ideally, you find a spot where you can see the Diary when you get up in the morning as well as before bedtime at night. For some people the best bet will be to keep the Diary within reach from their bed, for example on the bedside table. For others, it makes more sense to place it right next to the toothbrush, the handbag or the backpack. Based on my own experience and on the feedback of our German readers, we also recommend that you combine the Diary with an entrenched ritual, such as having your morning coffee or tea. Find out what works best for you. But make sure to try and find that perfect spot: You'll be surprised at how effective this small prompt will turn out to be.

Tip 2: Be detailed. Feel what you are writing

Since the structure of your Diary entries doesn't vary from day to day, it's likely that your entries may become repetitive. In principle, that is not a bad thing. In some instances – for example with the Jackhammer Approach you read about in the chapter on positive affirmation – it can actually be very useful. Yet, in other cases it's impractical to repeat yourself too frequently. What can you do to avoid writing down the same things over and over again? The solution is really simple: Be detailed! And most importantly, enjoy it!

It is more about the feelings you have whilst writing than the content itself. Thinking of things you're grateful for normally doesn't take that much time, but to feel the emotion you associate with these things, you usually need a few more seconds. Neuropsychologist Rick Hanson found that positive experiences have to be held in our awareness for about ten seconds or more in order to be transferred from short-term to long-term memory – while negative experiences immediately go into the long-term memory.[56] **This is why consciously taking those few extra seconds will help you turn a passing mental state into a lasting neural structure.** So take your time and wait for the emotion (the joy, the delight, the astonishment,...) before you put pen to paper. This can make a significant difference!

Think of a novel that captivates you. Good authors typically don't describe events in a general way, but in detail. They don't simply write, "She saw him," but rather something along the lines of: "When their eyes met, a shiver went down her back and though their lips did not meet, it felt as if she was kissing him with her breath." Of course this example is a little exaggerated, but it serves to illustrate the point: Emotion is contained in the details, and the more you go into detail when you describe something, the easier it is to feel those emotions.

> *If in the whole you wish to delight,*
> *the whole in the smallest you must find.*
> JOHANN WOLFGANG VON GOETHE

Maybe you wrote yesterday, "I'm grateful to have Rita by my side," then today you can write "I'm grateful that Rita keeps meeting new people and then introduces me to them," or, "I'm grateful that Rita always gives me that special smile when we visit other people." The same applies to the other sections of the Diary, especially to the great things you experienced today. What do you do if your day was anything but great, though? – Exactly. The solution is in the details again. Even when things seem crappy, you can still focus on the really small things, the glimpses of light on a dark day. Let your day pass in front of your mind's eye from the moment you got up, and look at it with the attitude that things could always be a lot worse. That way you will think of things such as, "My favourite Coldplay song was on the radio," or, "The cancelled meeting gave me more time to prepare my presentation." Even things like, "Avocados were on sale today," or, "The delicious chicken I had for lunch;" in short: Small, but mighty things. It does not matter if it's on a bad or good day – creating more awareness for the little details of life is always a good thing.

Writing into the Diary and filling in the gaps is supposed to be fun, so let your emotions run free. The deeper you dig into yourself, the stronger and more lasting the results will be for you. And the more You practise, the easier and faster this process will happen for You.

66

> **The magic is in the detail.**
> THEODOR FONTANE

Tip 3: Be ahead of the game and prepare NOW for later

Allocating three minutes in the morning and three minutes in the evening reduces the inhibition threshold to writing drastically. Still, there is always one element of risk, which might mean that your Diary ends up being nothing but a pretty and purely decorative item on your shelf.

Take a few minutes now and eliminate this small risk, too.

What might keep you from using the Diary every morning and evening?

1. _____

2. _____

3. _____

Now write down concrete measures that will enable you to overcome precisely those obstacles:

1. _____

2. _____

3. _____

As 70% of our sensory receptors are in our eyes and half our brain capacity is involved in visual processing[57], a visual reminder can also be a very effective tool. You could use The Weekly Habit-Tracker or tick off one day in your calendar once you've filled in your Morning and Evening Routine. There are also many apps that can help you stick to the daily use: *Habit List* or *Strides* may be useful if you have an iPhone, while Android users may find *Habit Bull* or *Loop Habit Tracker* helpful.

Tip 4: The structure is not set in stone

Football has a fixed set of rules, officially referred to as the "laws of the game". And yet, within that clear set of rules, each player has his very own way of playing. The same applies to the playing field of *The 6-Minute Diary*: Make your own rules and bring some variety into your *6-Minute Diary*. For example, you could plan to write down three totally new things you're grateful for every day – for one entire week. Accordingly, you can't list any of these things for a second time during that same week. An exercise like this helps to condition your perception (your RAS, p.52) in such way that you continually filter out the good aspects of any new situation, and thus see the opportunities and possibilities it holds for you. **By coming up with three totally new things you're grateful for, you will end up with a full week of unique reasons to be happy.**

The point of writing down three things you're grateful for in the morning is not to hastily jot down a shopping list of gratitude. If you approach your daily gratitude this way, it can quickly become repetitive resulting in your gratitude being processed in your head instead of your heart. As explained in Tip #2: You have to feel what you're writing. Since detailed entries are a great tool for achieving emotional connection, some days will call for more space to write it all down. If that is the case, you can simply cross out the numbers 1 to 3 and use the space for a longer gratitude entry. Of course the same applies to all the other sections in the Diary. The crucial part is that you feel emotionally connected to what you're writing. Over time, you'll find your own rhythm, which is going to feel natural and intuitively right for you.

Tip 5: Teamwork makes the dream work

Look for a partner in crime. Ben has Jerry, Batman has Robin, Bert has Ernie and Bonnie had Clyde. Take someone on board who has the same or a similar goal like you, a person for whom *The 6-Minute Diary* may be just as valuable as it will be for you. An alliance of two people who have their eyes on the same goal is very helpful and can encourage you to a great extent. Compare your experiences, hold each other accountable, help and motivate each other.

But even if you start out on your own, your friends and family can help you. Simply tell a few people about your *6-Minute Diary* project every day. That way, you hold yourself accountable and build a bit of gentle pressure, which can be very helpful in making sure you're adhering to it.[58] After all, you'll want to show the others that you are achieving what you announced you would, that you actually walk the talk. In addition to that, you may even inspire other people to come on board and pursue their own goals, too.

Tip 6: Form categories

After all, you're only human, too, so you will probably reach a point where you won't use *The 6-Minute Diary* every single day. If that doesn't happen: Fantastic! If it does, you should kick the all-or-nothing approach because all it will produce is usually no progress and a bad conscience. Instead of feeling bad about it, give yourself permission to do less: for example, allow yourself to do your favourite section or reduce the entries per section. The beautiful thing is: Once you take that small action, you gain momentum that will effortlessly carry you back to your usual 6-Minute rhythm.

> *Make it so easy you can't say no.*
> LEO BAUBAUTA

Even if you use the Diary every day and have the best intentions to always be emotionally involved in your entries, writer's block is bound to hit you at some point. When that happens, you can either take a little more time to feel what you're writing or – since you probably don't have all the time in the world – you can try something that's less time-consuming: Instead of spontaneously writing down what you feel grateful for, you can direct your gratitude to certain areas of your life. Simply form your very own categories such as:

1. Your health: exercise, digestion, nutrition, breathing, spirituality, sleep,...
2. Personal relationships: family, friends, partners, parents, colleagues, customers, dogs, cats,...
3. Events: something great that happened last week, month, semester, year.../ something great that (hopefully) will happen next week, month,...
4. Nature: birds chirping, beautiful clouds, flowers blooming, the golden red sunset, the smell of freshly cut grass, the sunshine on your skin,...
5. The simple things in life: seeing strangers laughing, your new playlist, the delicate touch of a kind person, the laughter of a baby, the cosy feeling of your favourite sweater,...

Focus on your family for a day or pay more attention to your friends for a week. You can also put the focus on an old relationship in your life that you value a lot. Let your creativity take you where you need to go. There is no recipe. Shape this Diary according to your needs and desires, maybe even turn it into your own personal "6-Minute Health Diary" or "6-Minute Relationship Diary" for a week. As always, the point here is to find the style that suits you and your current needs best. Many roads lead to Rome and likewise, many roads lead to happier and more fulfilled life.

"

Action may not always bring happiness, but there is no happiness without action.

WILLIAM JAMES

The
Diary

... enough chit-chat, now it's your turn. Time to take action!

Before you start, rate the following areas of your life (1 = worst possible / 10 = best possible). Then, add an arrow right next to the scale to show if the area is getting better or worse. You'll do this evaluation every 4 weeks.

Example:

Gratitude: 1   2   3   4   5   6   (7)   8   9   10   →

YOUR MONTHLY CHECK

Overall Mood:	1	2	3	4	5	6	7	8	9	10
Gratitude:	1	2	3	4	5	6	7	8	9	10
Mindfulness:	1	2	3	4	5	6	7	8	9	10
Family:	1	2	3	4	5	6	7	8	9	10
Friends:	1	2	3	4	5	6	7	8	9	10
Partnership:	1	2	3	4	5	6	7	8	9	10
Having Fun:	1	2	3	4	5	6	7	8	9	10
Calm & Serenity:	1	2	3	4	5	6	7	8	9	10
Time for You:	1	2	3	4	5	6	7	8	9	10
Eating Healthy:	1	2	3	4	5	6	7	8	9	10
Drinking Water:	1	2	3	4	5	6	7	8	9	10
Exercise & Movement:	1	2	3	4	5	6	7	8	9	10
Going Outside:	1	2	3	4	5	6	7	8	9	10
Health:	1	2	3	4	5	6	7	8	9	10
Creativity:	1	2	3	4	5	6	7	8	9	10
Finances:	1	2	3	4	5	6	7	8	9	10
Work & Education:	1	2	3	4	5	6	7	8	9	10
Thoughts & Emotions:	1	2	3	4	5	6	7	8	9	10
The Present:	1	2	3	4	5	6	7	8	9	10
The Future:	1	2	3	4	5	6	7	8	9	10

You've already heard of it: the almighty power of habits. As of now, you can use it to steer your own habits in the right direction. Which positive habits do you want to establish? – Go to the gym every other day, quit smoking, read 20 minutes or give three high fives a day... No matter if you want to track existing habits, get rid of old ones or bring new positive habits into your life, the Habit-Tracker is a proven system to help you achieve these goals.

Example:

HABIT	M	T	W	T	F	S	S	
flight mode after 10pm	✕	●	●	✕	●	✕	✕	
meditate 10 minutes	✕	✕	✕	✕	✕	✕	✕	😃

YOUR HABIT-TRACKER

HABIT	M	T	W	T	F	S	S
	●	●	●	●	●	●	●
	●	●	●	●	●	●	●
	●	●	●	●	●	●	●

"

We are what we repeatedly do.
Excellence, then, is not an act but a habit.

ARISTOTELES

What is currently your biggest worry? Imagine it wasn't your worry,
but that of your best friend. What advice would you give him/her?

_____

_____

_____

_____

_____

_____

Based on your daily routines and actions, where do you see
yourself in five years? What kind of person will you be if you
keep doing what you're doing right now?

_____

_____

_____

_____

_____

Who is your closest friend at the moment? What is it about him/her that you
are most grateful for? What do you think they appreciate most about you?

_____

_____

_____

_____

Let's travel back in time: If you had the chance to call the 10-year younger
You and talk for 30 seconds, what advice would you give your past self?

_____

_____

_____

When was the last time you cried tears of joy? What about the
last time you got goose bumps from a positive experience?

_____

_____

_____

NOTES & IDEAS

I'm grateful for...

1. _____
2. _____
3. _____

This is how I'll make today great

_____
_____
_____
_____
_____

Positive affirmation

_____
_____

Weekly challenge:

Write an email to the future that you will receive after completing your first *6-Minute Diary*. Describe where you see yourself and your life at that point in time (in approx. 6 months). You can write the mail on *futureme.org* or *whensend.com* for example.

My good deed today

_____
_____

How I'll improve

_____
_____

Great things I experienced today

1. _____
2. _____
3. _____

I'm grateful for…

1. _____
2. _____
3. _____

This is how I'll make today great

_____
_____
_____
_____
_____

Positive affirmation

_____
_____

> *The best way to predict your future is to create it.*
> ABRAHAM LINCOLN

My good deed today

_____
_____

How I'll improve

_____
_____

Great things I experienced today

1. _____
2. _____
3. _____

I'm grateful for…

1. _____
2. _____
3. _____

This is how I'll make today great

_____
_____
_____
_____
_____

Positive affirmation

_____
_____

> *Gratitude makes sense of our past, brings peace for today, and creates a vision for tomorrow.*
> MELODY BEATTIE

My good deed today

_____
_____

How I'll improve

_____
_____

Great things I experienced today

1. _____
2. _____
3. _____

I'm grateful for…

1. _____
2. _____
3. _____

This is how I'll make today great

_____
_____
_____
_____
_____

Positive affirmation

_____
_____

> *Life is not measured by the number of breaths we take, but by the moments that take our breath away.*
>
> MAYA ANGELOU

My good deed today

_____
_____

How I'll improve

_____
_____

Great things I experienced today

1. _____
2. _____
3. _____

I'm grateful for…

1. _____
2. _____
3. _____

This is how I'll make today great

_____
_____
_____
_____
_____

Positive affirmation

_____
_____

> *It is better to take many small steps
> in the right direction than to make a great leap
> forward only to stumble backward.*
> CHINESE PROVERB

My good deed today

_____
_____

How I'll improve

_____
_____

Great things I experienced today

1. _____
2. _____
3. _____

I'm grateful for...

1. _____
2. _____
3. _____

This is how I'll make today great

_____
_____
_____
_____
_____
_____

Positive affirmation

_____
_____

> *It's our choices, that show what we truly are, far more than our abilities.*
> J.K. ROWLING

My good deed today

_____
_____

How I'll improve

_____
_____

Great things I experienced today

1. _____
2. _____
3. _____

I'm grateful for...

1. _____
2. _____
3. _____

This is how I'll make today great

_____
_____
_____
_____
_____

Positive affirmation

_____
_____

> *An optimist does not stand in the rain,*
> *he is taking a shower under a cloud.*
> THOMAS ROMANUS

My good deed today

_____
_____

How I'll improve

_____
_____

Great things I experienced today

1. _____
2. _____
3. _____

5 WEEKLY QUESTIONS

According to Jim Rohn, you're the average of the 5 people you spend
most of your time with. Who are these people for you at the moment?
To what extent do they reflect who you are?

_____

_____

_____

_____

_____

_____

_____

What do you love and like most about yourself and why?
(Feel free to use the space on the next page).

_____

_____

_____

_____

_____

Which compliment had a huge influence on you? How did it
influence your life? When was the last time you complimented
someone else and they were really happy to hear it?

_____

_____

_____

_____

Which conversation topic can you immerse yourself in for hours?
When was the last time you talked about it?

_____

_____

_____

What would you do right away if you weren't afraid of making mistakes?

_____

_____

NOTES & IDEAS

_____
_____
_____
_____
_____
_____
_____
_____
_____
_____
_____
_____
_____
_____
_____
_____
_____
_____
_____
_____
_____
_____
_____

HABIT-TRACKER

HABIT	M	T	W	T	F	S	S
	●	●	●	●	●	●	●
	●	●	●	●	●	●	●
	●	●	●	●	●	●	●

I'm grateful for...

1. _____
2. _____
3. _____

This is how I'll make today great

_____
_____
_____
_____
_____

Positive affirmation

_____
_____

Weekly Challenge:

Isn't it always the unexpected pleasures which turn out to be the best ones? Your random acts of kindness can make someone else's entire day. So, go ahead and do something nice for a person who would never expect it.

My good deed today

_____
_____

How I'll improve

_____
_____

Great things I experienced today

1. _____
2. _____
3. _____

I'm grateful for…

1. _____
2. _____
3. _____

This is how I'll make today great

_____
_____
_____
_____
_____

Positive affirmation

_____
_____

> *Let your good deeds be like rain.*
> *Drop a little everywhere.*
> M. NASIRUDDIN AL-ALBANI

My good deed today

_____
_____

How I'll improve

_____
_____

Great things I experienced today

1. _____
2. _____
3. _____

I'm grateful for…

1. _____
2. _____
3. _____

This is how I'll make today great

_____
_____
_____
_____
_____

Positive affirmation

_____
_____

A drop of love is more than an ocean of intellect.
BLAISE PASCAL

My good deed today

_____
_____

How I'll improve

_____
_____

Great things I experienced today

1. _____
2. _____
3. _____

I'm grateful for…

1. _____
2. _____
3. _____

This is how I'll make today great

_____
_____
_____
_____
_____

Positive affirmation

_____
_____

> *The habit of looking on the bright side of every event is worth more than a thousand pounds per year.*
> SAMUEL JOHNSON

My good deed today

_____
_____

How I'll improve

_____
_____

Great things I experienced today

1. _____
2. _____
3. _____

I'm grateful for…

1. _____
2. _____
3. _____

This is how I'll make today great

_____
_____
_____
_____
_____

Positive affirmation

_____
_____

> ## The man who moves a mountain begins by carrying away small stones.
> CONFUCIUS

My good deed today

_____
_____

How I'll improve

_____
_____

Great things I experienced today

1. _____
2. _____
3. _____

I'm grateful for...

1. _____
2. _____
3. _____

This is how I'll make today great

_____
_____
_____
_____
_____

Positive affirmation

_____
_____

> *Being honest may not get you a lot of friends but it'll always get you the right ones.*
>
> JOHN LENNON

My good deed today

_____
_____

How I'll improve

_____
_____

Great things I experienced today

1. _____
2. _____
3. _____

I'm grateful for...

1. _____
2. _____
3. _____

This is how I'll make today great

_____
_____
_____
_____
_____
_____

Positive affirmation

_____
_____

> *The secret of change is to focus all of your energy,*
> *not on fighting the old, but on building the new.*
> SOCRATES

My good deed today

_____
_____

How I'll improve

_____
_____

Great things I experienced today

1. _____
2. _____
3. _____

5 WEEKLY QUESTIONS

What are currently the top 3 priorities in your life? What do you truly want
to focus your time and energy on? (If you'd like to have your priorities
at a glance, feel free to use the space at the end of this book).

_____

_____

_____

_____

_____

In what way are you spending too much time on things that aren't
your priorities and how could you reduce this time? Create a Not-Do-List
to increase awareness for your priorities (Here, too, you can use
the space for notes at the end of this book).

_____

_____

_____

_____

_____

What do you spend too much time worrying about? Will it be
relevant in 5 years? Will it matter in 5 weeks? Or even in 5 days?

_____

_____

_____

In your opinion, what do most people think within the
first seconds when they meet you for the first time?

_____

_____

_____

Do you think you have to achieve something in
order to be worth something? Why is that?

_____

_____

_____

NOTES & IDEAS

HABIT-TRACKER

HABIT	M	T	W	T	F	S	S

I'm grateful for...

1. _____
2. _____
3. _____

This is how I'll make today great

_____
_____
_____
_____
_____

Positive affirmation

_____
_____

Weekly challenge:

The stoic philosopher Seneca said: We suffer more from imagination than from reality. 2000 years later, a study proves him right by showing that only 15% of the things we worry about actually turn into reality, while 80% of these realities can be solved much easier than initially expected.[59] So keep in mind that the glass is really half-full and go through your day more optimistically.

My good deed today

_____
_____

How I'll improve

_____
_____

Great things I experienced today

1. _____
2. _____
3. _____

I'm grateful for…

1. _____
2. _____
3. _____

This is how I'll make today great

_____
_____
_____
_____
_____

Positive affirmation

_____
_____

> *Man is not worried by real problems so much as by his imagined anxieties about real problems.*
> EPICTETUS

My good deed today

_____
_____

How I'll improve

_____
_____

Great things I experienced today

1. _____
2. _____
3. _____

I'm grateful for…

1. _____
2. _____
3. _____

This is how I'll make today great

_____
_____
_____
_____
_____
_____

Positive affirmation

_____
_____
_____

> *Do not spoil what you have by desiring what you have not; remember that what you now have was once among the things you only hoped for.*
>
> EPICURUS

My good deed today

_____
_____

How I'll improve

_____
_____

Great things I experienced today

1. _____
2. _____
3. _____

I'm grateful for…

1. _____
2. _____
3. _____

This is how I'll make today great

_____
_____
_____
_____
_____

Positive affirmation

_____
_____

> *Most people overestimate what they can do in one year and underestimate what they can do in ten years.*
>
> BILL GATES

My good deed today

_____
_____

How I'll improve

_____
_____

Great things I experienced today

1. _____
2. _____
3. _____

I'm grateful for...

1. _____
2. _____
3. _____

This is how I'll make today great

_____
_____
_____
_____
_____

Positive affirmation

_____
_____

The biggest challenge in life is to be yourself in a world that is trying to make you like everyone else.

RALPH WALDO EMERSON

My good deed today

_____
_____

How I'll improve

_____
_____

Great things I experienced today

1. _____
2. _____
3. _____

I'm grateful for…

1. _____

2. _____

3. _____

This is how I'll make today great

_____

_____

_____

_____

_____

Positive affirmation

_____

_____

> *The highest reward for a person's toil is not what they get for it, but what they become by it.*
>
> JOHN RUSKIN

My good deed today

_____

_____

How I'll improve

_____

_____

Great things I experienced today

1. _____

2. _____

3. _____

I'm grateful for…

1. _____
2. _____
3. _____

This is how I'll make today great

_____
_____
_____
_____
_____

Positive affirmation

_____
_____

> *Such as are your habitual thoughts, such also will be the character of your mind; for the soul is dyed by the thought.*
>
> MARCUS AURELIUS

My good deed today

_____
_____

How I'll improve

_____
_____

Great things I experienced today

1. _____
2. _____
3. _____

5 WEEKLY QUESTIONS

You have flaws? So does everyone else. Your flaws make
you just as unique as your strengths. What are your flaws?
Write them down to embrace, celebrate and be proud of them!

_____

_____

_____

_____

_____

_____

Think of the 5 people you spend most of your time with. To what extent do
they give you energy when you are with them? List and rank them intuitively
from 1 to 10 (1 = they never... / 10 = they always give you energy).

Example: Ben ⟶ 9, he always makes me laugh and boosts my mood.

1. _____

2. _____

3. _____

4. _____

5. _____

When was the last time you were about to give up on something?
What kept you from actually giving up in the end?

_____

_____

_____

_____

What would you do with your time if you had to spend two years in prison?

_____

_____

_____

Who and what makes you laugh the most?

_____

_____

NOTES & IDEAS

_____
_____
_____
_____
_____
_____
_____
_____
_____
_____
_____
_____
_____
_____
_____
_____
_____
_____
_____
_____
_____
_____
_____
_____

HABIT-TRACKER

HABIT	M	T	W	T	F	S	S
	●	●	●	●	●	●	●
	●	●	●	●	●	●	●
	●	●	●	●	●	●	●

I'm grateful for…

1. _____
2. _____
3. _____

This is how I'll make today great

_____
_____
_____
_____
_____
_____

Positive affirmation

_____
_____

Weekly challenge:
This week, you are the positive counterpart:
If you notice somebody speaking badly about someone,
be the one who is saying something nice about that person.

My good deed today

_____
_____

How I'll improve

_____
_____

Great things I experienced today

1. _____
2. _____
3. _____

I'm grateful for…

1. _____
2. _____
3. _____

This is how I'll make today great

_____
_____
_____
_____
_____

Positive affirmation

_____
_____

The one who plants trees, knowing that he will never sit in their shade, has at least started to understand the meaning of life.

RABINDRANATH TAGORE

My good deed today

_____
_____

How I'll improve

_____
_____

Great things I experienced today

1. _____
2. _____
3. _____

I'm grateful for...

1. _____
2. _____
3. _____

This is how I'll make today great

_____
_____
_____
_____
_____

Positive affirmation

_____
_____

> *What lies behind us and what lies before us are tiny matters compared to what lies within us.*
> RALPH WALDO EMERSON

My good deed today

_____
_____

How I'll improve

_____
_____

Great things I experienced today

1. _____
2. _____
3. _____

I'm grateful for...

1. _____
2. _____
3. _____

This is how I'll make today great

_____
_____
_____
_____
_____

Positive affirmation

_____
_____

> *An archaeologist is the best husband a woman can have.*
> *The older she gets the more interested he is in her.*
>
> AGATHA CHRISTIE

My good deed today

_____
_____

How I'll improve

_____
_____

Great things I experienced today

1. _____
2. _____
3. _____

I'm grateful for...

1. _____
2. _____
3. _____

This is how I'll make today great

_____
_____
_____
_____
_____

Positive affirmation

_____
_____

> **When you change the way you look at things,
> the things you look at change.**
> WAYNE DYER

My good deed today

_____
_____

How I'll improve

_____
_____

Great things I experienced today

1. _____
2. _____
3. _____

I'm grateful for...

1. _____
2. _____
3. _____

This is how I'll make today great

_____
_____
_____
_____
_____

Positive affirmation

_____
_____

> *I have not failed.*
> *I've just found 10,000 ways that won't work.*
> THOMAS A. EDISON

My good deed today

_____
_____

How I'll improve

_____
_____

Great things I experienced today

1. _____
2. _____
3. _____

I'm grateful for...

1. _____
2. _____
3. _____

This is how I'll make today great

_____
_____
_____
_____
_____

Positive affirmation

_____
_____

Don't cry because it's over, smile because it happened.
DR. SEUSS

My good deed today

_____
_____

How I'll improve

_____
_____

Great things I experienced today

1. _____
2. _____
3. _____

5 WEEKLY QUESTIONS

Which of your personality traits and achievements are you really proud of?
What in particular makes you feel so proud of them?

_____

_____

_____

_____

_____

_____

_____

Which situations cause the most stress and tension in your everyday life?
What can you do – or stop doing – to approach them in a calmer way?

_____

_____

_____

_____

_____

If you could change your gender for one day, what would you like to do?
What would you be looking forward to most?

_____

_____

_____

_____

Who were the three or four most important people in your life ten years ago?
Who are they now and what has or hasn't changed?

_____

_____

_____

When was the last time you did something that nobody expected
you to do – not even yourself? How did that make you feel?

_____

_____

_____

MONTHLY CHECK

Overall Mood:	1	2	3	4	5	6	7	8	9	10
Gratitude:	1	2	3	4	5	6	7	8	9	10
Mindfulness:	1	2	3	4	5	6	7	8	9	10
Family:	1	2	3	4	5	6	7	8	9	10
Friends:	1	2	3	4	5	6	7	8	9	10
Partnership:	1	2	3	4	5	6	7	8	9	10
Having Fun:	1	2	3	4	5	6	7	8	9	10
Calm & Serenity:	1	2	3	4	5	6	7	8	9	10
Time for You:	1	2	3	4	5	6	7	8	9	10
Eating Healthy:	1	2	3	4	5	6	7	8	9	10
Drinking Water:	1	2	3	4	5	6	7	8	9	10
Exercise & Movement:	1	2	3	4	5	6	7	8	9	10
Going Outside:	1	2	3	4	5	6	7	8	9	10
Health:	1	2	3	4	5	6	7	8	9	10
Creativity:	1	2	3	4	5	6	7	8	9	10
Finances:	1	2	3	4	5	6	7	8	9	10
Work & Education:	1	2	3	4	5	6	7	8	9	10
Thoughts & Emotions:	1	2	3	4	5	6	7	8	9	10
The Present:	1	2	3	4	5	6	7	8	9	10
The Future:	1	2	3	4	5	6	7	8	9	10

MONTHLY NOTES

NOTES & IDEAS

_____
_____
_____
_____
_____
_____
_____
_____
_____
_____
_____
_____
_____
_____
_____
_____
_____
_____
_____
_____
_____
_____
_____
_____
_____

HABIT-TRACKER

HABIT	M	T	W	T	F	S	S
	●	●	●	●	●	●	●
	●	●	●	●	●	●	●
	●	●	●	●	●	●	●

I'm grateful for…

1. _____
2. _____
3. _____

This is how I'll make today great

_____
_____
_____
_____
_____

Positive affirmation

_____
_____

Weekly challenge:

Do you know what Leonardo da Vinci, Eleanor Roosevelt, Bill Clinton, Margaret Thatcher & Albert Einstein have in common? They all take (or took) daily naps. In fact, the right to nap is even anchored in the Constitution of Japan. Treat yourself to occasional 20-minute naps and enjoy the benefits such as a boost in concentration, improved memory & reduced stress levels.

My good deed today

_____
_____

How I'll improve

_____
_____

Great things I experienced today

1. _____
2. _____
3. _____

I'm grateful for...

1. _____
2. _____
3. _____

This is how I'll make today great

_____
_____
_____
_____
_____

Positive affirmation

_____
_____

> *The art of relaxing is part of the art of working.*
> JOHN STEINBECK

My good deed today

_____
_____

How I'll improve

_____
_____

Great things I experienced today

1. _____
2. _____
3. _____

I'm grateful for...

1. _____
2. _____
3. _____

This is how I'll make today great

_____
_____
_____
_____
_____

Positive affirmation

_____
_____

> *You have to take people as they are because there are no others.*
>
> KONRAD ADENAUER

My good deed today

_____
_____

How I'll improve

_____
_____

Great things I experienced today

1. _____
2. _____
3. _____

I'm grateful for...

1. _____
2. _____
3. _____

This is how I'll make today great

_____
_____
_____
_____
_____

Positive affirmation

_____
_____

> *One day you will wake up and there won't be any more time to do the things you've always wanted to do. Do them now.*
>
> PAULO COELHO

My good deed today

_____
_____

How I'll improve

_____
_____

Great things I experienced today

1. _____
2. _____
3. _____

I'm grateful for…

1. _____
2. _____
3. _____

This is how I'll make today great

_____
_____
_____
_____
_____

Positive affirmation

_____
_____

> *People will forget what you said.*
> *People will forget what you did. But people*
> *will never forget how you made them feel.*
>
> MAYA ANGELOU

My good deed today

_____
_____

How I'll improve

_____
_____

Great things I experienced today

1. _____
2. _____
3. _____

I'm grateful for…

1. _____
2. _____
3. _____

This is how I'll make today great

_____
_____
_____
_____
_____

Positive affirmation

_____
_____

Let yourself be silently drawn by the strange pull of what you really love. It will not lead you astray.
RUMI

My good deed today

_____
_____

How I'll improve

_____
_____

Great things I experienced today

1. _____
2. _____
3. _____

I'm grateful for…

1. _____
2. _____
3. _____

This is how I'll make today great

_____
_____
_____
_____
_____

Positive affirmation

_____
_____

> *If we meet someone who owes us a debt of gratitude, we remember the fact at once. How often we can meet someone to whom we owe a debt of gratitude without thinking about it at all.*
>
> JOHANN WOLFGANG VON GOETHE

My good deed today

_____
_____

How I'll improve

_____
_____

Great things I experienced today

1. _____
2. _____
3. _____

5 WEEKLY QUESTIONS

I say "life", you say...? – Don't think, just write down the first words
that cross your mind. You may be surprised by what you can learn
about yourself when you let your intuition guide you:

Life: _____

Humour: _____

Fear: _____

Love: _____

Sadness: _____

Honesty: _____

Future: _____

Why did you choose the profession you're pursuing?
Are you doing what you truly want to do?

_____

_____

_____

_____

_____

At what age were you the happiest so far?
What was (is) so special about that time?

_____

_____

_____

_____

Which bad habit is currently diminishing your quality of life?
What positive habit can you build to replace it? And why not use
the weekly Habit-Tracker to help you entrench this new habit?

_____

_____

_____

If you could witness any event in the past or in the future, what would it be?

_____

_____

NOTES & IDEAS

_____
_____
_____
_____
_____
_____
_____
_____
_____
_____
_____
_____
_____
_____
_____
_____
_____
_____
_____
_____
_____
_____
_____
_____
_____

HABIT-TRACKER

HABIT	M	T	W	T	F	S	S
	●	●	●	●	●	●	●
	●	●	●	●	●	●	●
	●	●	●	●	●	●	●

I'm grateful for…

1. _____
2. _____
3. _____

This is how I'll make today great

_____
_____
_____
_____
_____

Positive affirmation

_____
_____

Weekly challenge:

Which person played the most important role in your life this past year? Why not express your gratitude to that person with a short message, a handwritten note or a phone call? Take a glimpse at "An Experiment in Gratitude" (The Science of Happiness) on *YouTube* and see for yourself how powerful your message could be.

My good deed today

_____
_____

How I'll improve

_____
_____

Great things I experienced today

1. _____
2. _____
3. _____

I'm grateful for…

1. _____
2. _____
3. _____

This is how I'll make today great

_____
_____
_____
_____
_____

Positive affirmation

_____
_____

> *Feeling gratitude and not expressing it is like wrapping a gift and not giving it.*
>
> WILLIAM ARTHUR WARD

My good deed today

_____
_____

How I'll improve

_____
_____

Great things I experienced today

1. _____
2. _____
3. _____

I'm grateful for…

1. _____
2. _____
3. _____

This is how I'll make today great

_____
_____
_____
_____
_____

Positive affirmation

_____
_____

There is no path to happiness.
Happiness is the path.

BUDDHA

My good deed today

_____
_____

How I'll improve

_____
_____

Great things I experienced today

1. _____
2. _____
3. _____

I'm grateful for...

1. _____
2. _____
3. _____

This is how I'll make today great

_____
_____
_____
_____
_____

Positive affirmation

_____
_____

> *If all the year were playing holidays,*
> *to play would be as tedious as to work.*
>
> WILLIAM SHAKESPEARE

My good deed today

_____
_____

How I'll improve

_____
_____

Great things I experienced today

1. _____
2. _____
3. _____

I'm grateful for...

1. _____
2. _____
3. _____

This is how I'll make today great

_____
_____
_____
_____
_____

Positive affirmation

_____
_____

> *Life is a great big canvas and you should
> throw all the paint you can on it.*
> DANNY KAYE

My good deed today

_____
_____

How I'll improve

_____
_____

Great things I experienced today

1. _____
2. _____
3. _____

I'm grateful for…

1. _____
2. _____
3. _____

This is how I'll make today great

_____
_____
_____
_____
_____

Positive affirmation

_____
_____

> *Never apologize for being yourself.*
> PAULO COELHO

My good deed today

_____
_____

How I'll improve

_____
_____

Great things I experienced today

1. _____
2. _____
3. _____

I'm grateful for…

1. _____
2. _____
3. _____

This is how I'll make today great

_____
_____
_____
_____
_____

Positive affirmation

_____
_____

> *A year from now you may wish you had started today.*
> KAREN LAMB

My good deed today

_____
_____

How I'll improve

_____
_____

Great things I experienced today

1. _____
2. _____
3. _____

5 WEEKLY QUESTIONS

What is the one goal you want to reach within the next year? Is this goal improving your present reality? What do you think will be different when you've reached it? Are your short-term efforts and your long-term goals aligned?

_____

_____

_____

_____

_____

_____

Think of something or someone important you recently lost.
What were two positive insights you gained from that experience?

_____

_____

_____

_____

_____

What's the best advice you've ever received?
What do you think was the best advice you've ever given to someone?

_____

_____

_____

_____

If you could use a gigantic, 330 ft wide billboard and place it anywhere you want, where would you put it? What would you display on it and why?

_____

_____

_____

What has your intuition been telling you that you might be ignoring?

_____

_____

_____

NOTES & IDEAS

HABIT-TRACKER

HABIT	M	T	W	T	F	S	S
	●	●	●	●	●	●	●
	●	●	●	●	●	●	●
	●	●	●	●	●	●	●

I'm grateful for...

1. _____
2. _____
3. _____

This is how I'll make today great

_____
_____
_____
_____
_____

Positive affirmation

_____
_____

Weekly challenge:

Many of the lessons you will eventually learn, have already been mastered by others. This is why more experienced people can teach you in minutes what would take weeks or months to learn on your own. Do you allow yourself to actively approach such people? This week you do. Get in touch with an experienced person and learn from his or her life lessons and wisdom.

My good deed today

_____
_____

How I'll improve

_____
_____

Great things I experienced today

1. _____
2. _____
3. _____

I'm grateful for…

1. _____
2. _____
3. _____

This is how I'll make today great

_____
_____
_____
_____
_____

Positive affirmation

_____
_____

> *You don't have to be great to start,*
> *but you have to start to be great.*
> ZIG ZIGLAR

My good deed today

_____
_____

How I'll improve

_____
_____

Great things I experienced today

1. _____
2. _____
3. _____

I'm grateful for...

1. _____
2. _____
3. _____

This is how I'll make today great

_____
_____
_____
_____
_____

Positive affirmation

_____
_____

> *The happiness of your life depends upon the quality of your thoughts.*
> MARCUS AURELIUS

My good deed today

_____
_____

How I'll improve

_____
_____

Great things I experienced today

1. _____
2. _____
3. _____

I'm grateful for…

1. _____
2. _____
3. _____

This is how I'll make today great

_____
_____
_____
_____
_____

Positive affirmation

_____
_____

> *If you want something you've never had, you must be willing to do something you've never done.*
> THOMAS JEFFERSON

My good deed today

_____
_____

How I'll improve

_____
_____

Great things I experienced today

1. _____
2. _____
3. _____

I'm grateful for...

1. _____
2. _____
3. _____

This is how I'll make today great

_____
_____
_____
_____
_____

Positive affirmation

_____
_____

The pessimist sees difficulty in every opportunity.
The optimist sees the opportunity in every difficulty.

WINSTON CHURCHILL

My good deed today

_____
_____

How I'll improve

_____
_____

Great things I experienced today

1. _____
2. _____
3. _____

I'm grateful for...

1. _____
2. _____
3. _____

This is how I'll make today great

_____
_____
_____
_____
_____

Positive affirmation

_____
_____

> *If everything you try works,*
> *you are not trying hard enough.*
>
> GORDON MOORE

My good deed today

_____
_____

How I'll improve

_____
_____

Great things I experienced today

1. _____
2. _____
3. _____

I'm grateful for…

1. _____
2. _____
3. _____

This is how I'll make today great

_____
_____
_____
_____
_____

Positive affirmation

_____
_____

> *Experience is a master teacher,*
> *even when it's not our own.*
> GINA GREENLEE

My good deed today

_____
_____

How I'll improve

_____
_____

Great things I experienced today

1. _____
2. _____
3. _____

When you think of the word "successful", who are the first two people that come to your mind and why? What does "success" mean to you personally?

_____

_____

_____

_____

_____

_____

What are your strengths? What comes more naturally to you than to others? How could you bring your life more into harmony with your strengths and abilities?

_____

_____

_____

_____

_____

What project is stashed away in your heart that deserves more time and dedication? What's one action you can take right now to bring it to life?

_____

_____

_____

_____

What are currently the two thoughts you most frequently have?

_____

_____

_____

_____

If you were on a speed date and there was only one thing that you could tell the other person about you, what would that be?

_____

_____

_____

NOTES & IDEAS

_____

_____

_____

_____

_____

_____

_____

_____

_____

_____

_____

_____

_____

_____

_____

_____

_____

_____

_____

_____

_____

_____

_____

_____

_____

HABIT-TRACKER

HABIT	M	T	W	T	F	S	S

I'm grateful for...

1. _____
2. _____
3. _____

This is how I'll make today great

Positive affirmation

Weekly challenge:

Ray Dalio, founder of *Bridgewater Associates*, the world's biggest hedge fund, stresses again and again that you have to acknowledge your weaknesses in order to live up to your potential. This week, spend ten minutes each day working on how to turn a weakness into a strength or alternatively, on finding people, tools or mechanisms to help you fill that gap.

My good deed today

How I'll improve

Great things I experienced today

1. _____
2. _____
3. _____

I'm grateful for…

1. _____
2. _____
3. _____

This is how I'll make today great

_____
_____
_____
_____
_____

Positive affirmation

_____
_____

> *Try to look at your weakness and convert it into your strength. That's success.*
> ZIG ZIGLAR

My good deed today

_____
_____

How I'll improve

_____
_____

Great things I experienced today

1. _____
2. _____
3. _____

I'm grateful for…

1. _____
2. _____
3. _____

This is how I'll make today great

_____
_____
_____
_____
_____

Positive affirmation

_____
_____

> *If you are distressed by anything external, the pain is not due to the thing itself, but to your estimate of it; and this you have the power to revoke at any moment.*
> MARCUS AURELIUS

My good deed today

_____
_____

How I'll improve

_____
_____

Great things I experienced today

1. _____
2. _____
3. _____

I'm grateful for…

1. _____
2. _____
3. _____

This is how I'll make today great

_____
_____
_____
_____
_____

Positive affirmation

_____
_____

> *A friend is someone who knows all about you and still loves you.*
> ELBERT HUBBARD

My good deed today

_____
_____

How I'll improve

_____
_____

Great things I experienced today

1. _____
2. _____
3. _____

I'm grateful for…

1. _____
2. _____
3. _____

This is how I'll make today great

_____
_____
_____
_____
_____

Positive affirmation

_____
_____

> *The world stands aside to let anyone pass who knows where he is going.*
> DAVID STARR JORDAN

My good deed today

_____
_____

How I'll improve

_____
_____

Great things I experienced today

1. _____
2. _____
3. _____

MTWTFSS _____

I'm grateful for…

1. _____
2. _____
3. _____

This is how I'll make today great

_____
_____
_____
_____
_____

Positive affirmation

_____
_____

> *It takes two years to learn to speak
> and sixty to learn to keep quiet.*
> ERNEST HEMINGWAY

My good deed today

_____
_____

How I'll improve

_____
_____

Great things I experienced today

1. _____
2. _____
3. _____

I'm grateful for…

1. _____
2. _____
3. _____

This is how I'll make today great

_____
_____
_____
_____
_____

Positive affirmation

_____
_____

Happiness is not something you postpone for the future; it's something you design for the present.
JIM ROHN

My good deed today

_____
_____

How I'll improve

_____
_____

Great things I experienced today

1. _____
2. _____
3. _____

5 WEEKLY QUESTIONS

If you close your eyes and imagine yourself 10 and then 20 years from now, how and where do you see yourself? A few years from now, it will be very interesting to read what you've written here today...

In 10 years: _____

_____

_____

In 20 years: _____

_____

_____

Who's had a greater influence on you, your mother or your father? What are the things you value most and least about their influence?

_____

_____

_____

_____

_____

How many hours a week did you work on average last year? Would you rather have less work to do or more work that you enjoy doing? Why is that?

_____

_____

_____

_____

"Wow, I totally forgot to have lunch!". Which activity did ever make you forget to eat or to go to the toilet because you were so deeply immersed in it?

_____

_____

_____

_____

What are your deepest and biggest fears? How likely are they to happen?

_____

_____

_____

MONTHLY CHECK

Overall Mood:	1	2	3	4	5	6	7	8	9	10
Gratitude:	1	2	3	4	5	6	7	8	9	10
Mindfulness:	1	2	3	4	5	6	7	8	9	10
Family:	1	2	3	4	5	6	7	8	9	10
Friends:	1	2	3	4	5	6	7	8	9	10
Partnership:	1	2	3	4	5	6	7	8	9	10
Having Fun:	1	2	3	4	5	6	7	8	9	10
Calm & Serenity:	1	2	3	4	5	6	7	8	9	10
Time for You:	1	2	3	4	5	6	7	8	9	10
Eating Healthy:	1	2	3	4	5	6	7	8	9	10
Drinking Water:	1	2	3	4	5	6	7	8	9	10
Exercise & Movement:	1	2	3	4	5	6	7	8	9	10
Going Outside:	1	2	3	4	5	6	7	8	9	10
Health:	1	2	3	4	5	6	7	8	9	10
Creativity:	1	2	3	4	5	6	7	8	9	10
Finances:	1	2	3	4	5	6	7	8	9	10
Work & Education:	1	2	3	4	5	6	7	8	9	10
Thoughts & Emotions:	1	2	3	4	5	6	7	8	9	10
The Present:	1	2	3	4	5	6	7	8	9	10
The Future:	1	2	3	4	5	6	7	8	9	10

MONTHLY NOTES

_____

_____

_____

_____

_____

_____

_____

_____

_____

NOTES & IDEAS

_____
_____
_____
_____
_____
_____
_____
_____
_____
_____
_____
_____
_____
_____
_____
_____
_____
_____
_____
_____
_____
_____
_____
_____

HABIT-TRACKER

HABIT	M	T	W	T	F	S	S
	●	●	●	●	●	●	●
	●	●	●	●	●	●	●
	●	●	●	●	●	●	●

I'm grateful for...

1. _____
2. _____
3. _____

This is how I'll make today great

_____
_____
_____
_____
_____

Positive affirmation

_____
_____

Weekly challenge:

How often do you have great ideas and flashes of inspiration, which then vanish within seconds? Too bad! This week, capture those "light bulb moments" in a little notebook or your phone. Numerous successful people like Bill Gates, Sheryl Sandberg, J.K. Rowling and Richard Branson share this great habit of recording their thoughts and ideas.

My good deed today

_____
_____

How I'll improve

_____
_____

Great things I experienced today

1. _____
2. _____
3. _____

I'm grateful for…

1. _____
2. _____
3. _____

This is how I'll make today great

_____
_____
_____
_____
_____

Positive affirmation

_____
_____

The mind is for having ideas, not for holding them.
DAVID ALLEN

My good deed today

_____
_____

How I'll improve

_____
_____

Great things I experienced today

1. _____
2. _____
3. _____

I'm grateful for…

1. _____
2. _____
3. _____

This is how I'll make today great

_____
_____
_____
_____
_____

Positive affirmation

_____
_____

"

Life is like riding a bicycle.
To keep your balance, you must keep moving.
ALBERT EINSTEIN

"

My good deed today

_____
_____

How I'll improve

_____
_____

Great things I experienced today

1. _____
2. _____
3. _____

I'm grateful for…

1. _____
2. _____
3. _____

This is how I'll make today great

_____
_____
_____
_____
_____

Positive affirmation

_____
_____

> *Life is about making an impact,*
> *not making an income.*
> KEVIN KRUSE

My good deed today

_____
_____

How I'll improve

_____
_____

Great things I experienced today

1. _____
2. _____
3. _____

I'm grateful for…

1. _____
2. _____
3. _____

This is how I'll make today great

_____
_____
_____
_____
_____

Positive affirmation

_____
_____

> *Many of life's failures are people who did not realize how close they were to success when they gave up.*
> THOMAS A. EDISON

My good deed today

_____
_____

How I'll improve

_____
_____

Great things I experienced today

1. _____
2. _____
3. _____

I'm grateful for…

1. _____
2. _____
3. _____

This is how I'll make today great

_____
_____
_____
_____
_____

Positive affirmation

_____
_____

> ## No one knows what he can do until he tries.
> POBILIUS SYRUS

My good deed today

_____
_____

How I'll improve

_____
_____

Great things I experienced today

1. _____
2. _____
3. _____

I'm grateful for...

1. _____
2. _____
3. _____

This is how I'll make today great

_____
_____
_____
_____
_____

Positive affirmation

_____
_____

> *You can close your eyes to the things you don't want to see, but you can't close your heart to the things you don't want to feel.*
> JOHNNY DEPP

My good deed today

_____
_____

How I'll improve

_____
_____

Great things I experienced today

1. _____
2. _____
3. _____

5 WEEKLY QUESTIONS

Are you currently in love? If not, when was the last time you were? What exactly does being in love mean to you and how do you feel when you're in love?

_____

_____

_____

_____

_____

What was the biggest challenge you had to face in the past year?
How did you overcome it?

_____

_____

_____

_____

Is there something that you wish you could leave behind?
What is the monkey on your back that you would like to get rid of?

_____

_____

_____

_____

What legacy do you want to leave behind?
What should others remember about you at the end of your life?
And if this is what's most important at the end, how important is it now?

_____

_____

_____

Imagine *you'd* receive a letter from the 10-year older You today.
What advice would your older version give yourself for the future?

_____

_____

_____

NOTES & IDEAS

_____
_____
_____
_____
_____
_____
_____
_____
_____
_____
_____
_____
_____
_____
_____
_____
_____
_____
_____
_____
_____
_____
_____
_____

HABIT-TRACKER

HABIT	M	T	W	T	F	S	S
	●	●	●	●	●	●	●
	●	●	●	●	●	●	●
	●	●	●	●	●	●	●

I'm grateful for…

1. _____
2. _____
3. _____

This is how I'll make today great

_____
_____
_____
_____
_____

Positive affirmation

_____
_____

Weekly challenge:

Do you sometimes interrupt others because you think you've got something important to say? This week, try to communicate mindfully: Listen with curiosity and without judgment. Let others finish speaking, breathe in and out gently, and only then – really only then – start talking. Observe how this technique will change your conversations and draw your own conclusions.

My good deed today

_____
_____

How I'll improve

_____
_____

Great things I experienced today

1. _____
2. _____
3. _____

I'm grateful for…

1. _____
2. _____
3. _____

This is how I'll make today great

_____
_____
_____
_____
_____

Positive affirmation

_____
_____

> *The greatest problem with communication is we don't listen to understand. We listen to reply. When we listen with curiosity, we don't listen with the intent to reply. We listen for what's behind the words.*
> ROY T. BENNETT

My good deed today

_____
_____

How I'll improve

_____
_____

Great things I experienced today

1. _____
2. _____
3. _____

I'm grateful for…

1. _____
2. _____
3. _____

This is how I'll make today great

_____
_____
_____
_____
_____

Positive affirmation

_____
_____

*Experience is not what happens to you;
it's what you do with what happens to you.*
ALDOUS HUXLEY

My good deed today

_____
_____

How I'll improve

_____
_____

Great things I experienced today

1. _____
2. _____
3. _____

66 Days

… The 6–Minute Diary is now part of you.

> *What one does is what counts.*
> *Not what one had the intention of doing.*
> PABLO PICASSO

You're actually doing it! If you're reading these lines, you're part of the small circle of Doers: the men and women of action. Wear your badge proudly! Enjoy this little milestone by treating yourself to something nice! Flip through the pages you've already filled and enjoy the view: the memories, the emotions and every little thing you've achieved until today.

Sixes after Sixes: You've been using *The 6-Minute Diary* for 66 days, so now is a good time to rest on your laurels for a moment. As you read in the Fundamentals, new habits are entrenched in your life after 66 days. **So *The 6-Minute Diary* is part of you now!**

Alright, so the time period may not be precisely accurate for every single habit and every single person, but the main thing is: You're definitely on the right path!

> *Happiness is the only thing that*
> *multiplies when you share it.*
> ALBERT SCHWEITZER

If you want to multiply your happiness, then let us be part of it :)

Take a snazzy snapshot of the little gem
in your hands and tag us on Instagram:

@createurbestself + #6minutediary

"

Habit is, as it were, a second nature.

MARCUS TULLIUS CICERO

I'm grateful for...

1. _____
2. _____
3. _____

This is how I'll make today great

_____
_____
_____
_____
_____

Positive affirmation

_____
_____

" *Not all of us can do great things.*
But we can do small things with great love.
MOTHER TERESA "

My good deed today

_____
_____

How I'll improve

_____
_____

Great things I experienced today

1. _____
2. _____
3. _____

I'm grateful for…

1. _____
2. _____
3. _____

This is how I'll make today great

_____
_____
_____
_____
_____
_____

Positive affirmation

_____
_____

> *The true meaning of life is to plant trees,*
> *under whose shade you do not expect to sit.*
> NELSON HENDERSON

My good deed today

_____
_____

How I'll improve

_____
_____

Great things I experienced today

1. _____
2. _____
3. _____

I'm grateful for...

1. _____
2. _____
3. _____

This is how I'll make today great

_____
_____
_____
_____
_____

Positive affirmation

_____
_____

> *Nothing that results in human progress is achieved with unanimous consent.*
> CHRISTOPHER COLUMBUS

My good deed today

_____
_____

How I'll improve

_____
_____

Great things I experienced today

1. _____
2. _____
3. _____

I'm grateful for...

1. _____
2. _____
3. _____

This is how I'll make today great

_____
_____
_____
_____
_____

Positive affirmation

_____
_____

> ## *If it scares you, it might be a good thing to try.*
> SETH GODIN

My good deed today

_____
_____

How I'll improve

_____
_____

Great things I experienced today

1. _____
2. _____
3. _____

5 WEEKLY QUESTIONS

What is your purpose in life? Why does it matter that you exist?

_____

_____

_____

_____

_____

_____

_____

What are the three things you like doing most with
your partner when you're in a relationship?

_____

_____

_____

_____

_____

_____

_____

Identify one aspect of your life that you wish was different. Now, can you come
up with at least one reason why you are grateful for that same aspect?

_____

_____

_____

Which trait do your parents and/or grandparents appreciate most about you?

_____

_____

_____

If you were a beggar, what would you write on your begging sign and why?

_____

_____

_____

NOTES & IDEAS

_____
_____
_____
_____
_____
_____
_____
_____
_____
_____
_____
_____
_____
_____
_____
_____
_____
_____
_____
_____
_____
_____
_____
_____
_____
_____

HABIT-TRACKER

HABIT	M	T	W	T	F	S	S
	●	●	●	●	●	●	●
	●	●	●	●	●	●	●
	●	●	●	●	●	●	●

I'm grateful for...

1. _____
2. _____
3. _____

This is how I'll make today great

_____
_____
_____
_____
_____

Positive affirmation

_____
_____

Weekly challenge:

We are judging about 35,000 times a day.[60] Whether it's the food we eat, the things we read or the people we meet – we put our personal label on people and things.[61] As unintended as these judgments might be, we can still be mindful about them! This week, try to avoid judging everything and everyone. Broaden your mind by simply letting things and people be.

My good deed today

_____
_____

HABIT-TRACKER

_____
_____

Great things I experienced today

1. _____
2. _____
3. _____

I'm grateful for...

1. _____
2. _____
3. _____

This is how I'll make today great

_____
_____
_____
_____
_____

Positive affirmation

_____
_____

> *Judging is preventing us from understanding a new truth. Free yourself from the rules of old judgments and create the space for new understanding.*
> STEVE MARABOLI

My good deed today

_____
_____

How I'll improve

_____
_____

Great things I experienced today

1. _____
2. _____
3. _____

I'm grateful for...

1. _____
2. _____
3. _____

This is how I'll make today great

_____
_____
_____
_____
_____
_____

Positive affirmation

_____
_____

> *Remember that sometimes not getting what you want is a wonderful stroke of luck.*
>
> DALAI LAMA

My good deed today

_____
_____

How I'll improve

_____
_____

Great things I experienced today

1. _____
2. _____
3. _____

I'm grateful for…

1. _____
2. _____
3. _____

This is how I'll make today great

_____
_____
_____
_____
_____

Positive affirmation

_____
_____

> ## *The shortest distance between two people is a smile.*
> VICTOR BORGE

My good deed today

_____
_____

How I'll improve

_____
_____

Great things I experienced today

1. _____
2. _____
3. _____

I'm grateful for...

1. _____
2. _____
3. _____

This is how I'll make today great

_____
_____
_____
_____
_____

Positive affirmation

_____
_____

> *Kindness in words creates confidence.*
> *Kindness in thinking creates profoundness.*
> *Kindness in giving creates love.*
> LAO TZU

My good deed today

_____
_____

How I'll improve

_____
_____

Great things I experienced today

1. _____
2. _____
3. _____

I'm grateful for…

1. _____
2. _____
3. _____

This is how I'll make today great

_____
_____
_____
_____
_____

Positive affirmation

_____
_____

> ## *For everything you have missed, you have gained something else.*
> RALPH WALDO EMERSON

My good deed today

_____
_____

How I'll improve

_____
_____

Great things I experienced today

1. _____
2. _____
3. _____

I'm grateful for...

1. _____
2. _____
3. _____

This is how I'll make today great

_____
_____
_____
_____
_____

Positive affirmation

_____
_____

> *Don't judge each day by the harvest you reap but by the seeds you plant.*
> ROBERT LOUIS STEVENSON

My good deed today

_____
_____

How I'll improve

_____
_____

Great things I experienced today

1. _____
2. _____
3. _____

5 WEEKLY QUESTIONS

Which lifelong dream have you fulfilled so far? What dream
do you want to fulfill most urgently within the next 5 to 10 years?
What concrete milestone can you start working towards already?

_____

_____

_____

_____

_____

_____

_____

How do you counter the breathless pace of our high-speed society?
What do you do to relax and unwind on a daily basis?

_____

_____

_____

_____

_____

Where do you feel most at home and what makes this place so special to you?

_____

_____

_____

_____

If you were to give a speech in front of 200,000 people,
what topic would you choose to speak about?

_____

_____

_____

What is the most mesmerizing thing you have ever seen?

_____

_____

NOTES & IDEAS

_____
_____
_____
_____
_____
_____
_____
_____
_____
_____
_____
_____
_____
_____
_____
_____
_____
_____
_____
_____
_____
_____
_____

HABIT-TRACKER

HABIT	M	T	W	T	F	S	S
	●	●	●	●	●	●	●
	●	●	●	●	●	●	●
	●	●	●	●	●	●	●

I'm grateful for…

1. _____
2. _____
3. _____

This is how I'll make today great

_____
_____
_____
_____
_____

Positive affirmation

_____
_____

Weekly challenge:

Studies show: The more profoundly you are able to relax, the better your ability to focus and to be productive.[62] So just as you plan to be productive with your to-do-list, you should proactively plan to unwind with your to-relax-list. This, week set aside fixed times to relax and take them as seriously as any other appointment.

My good deed today

_____
_____

How I'll improve

_____
_____

Great things I experienced today

1. _____
2. _____
3. _____

I'm grateful for…

1. _____
2. _____
3. _____

This is how I'll make today great

_____
_____
_____
_____
_____

Positive affirmation

_____
_____

Your ability to generate power is directly proportional to your ability to relax.

DAVID ALLEN

My good deed today

_____
_____

How I'll improve

_____
_____

Great things I experienced today

1. _____
2. _____
3. _____

I'm grateful for…

1. _____
2. _____
3. _____

This is how I'll make today great

_____
_____
_____
_____
_____
_____

Positive affirmation

_____
_____
_____

Be not afraid of growing slowly;
be afraid only of standing still.
CHINESE PROVERB

My good deed today

_____
_____

How I'll improve

_____
_____

Great things I experienced today

1. _____
2. _____
3. _____

I'm grateful for…

1. _____
2. _____
3. _____

This is how I'll make today great

_____
_____
_____
_____
_____

Positive affirmation

_____
_____

> *Dance like nobody's watching. Love like you've never been hurt. Sing like nobody's listening. Live like it's heaven on earth.*
>
> MARK TWAIN

My good deed today

_____
_____

How I'll improve

_____
_____

Great things I experienced today

1. _____
2. _____
3. _____

I'm grateful for…

1. _____
2. _____
3. _____

This is how I'll make today great

_____
_____
_____
_____
_____

Positive affirmation

_____
_____

> *There is nothing in the world so irresistibly contagious as laughter and good humour.*
> CHARLES DICKENS

My good deed today

_____
_____

How I'll improve

_____
_____

Great things I experienced today

1. _____
2. _____
3. _____

I'm grateful for...

1. _____
2. _____
3. _____

This is how I'll make today great

_____
_____
_____
_____
_____

Positive affirmation

_____
_____

> *The summit of happiness is reached when a person is ready to be what he is.*
> ERASMUS OF ROTTERDAM

My good deed today

_____
_____

How I'll improve

_____
_____

Great things I experienced today

1. _____
2. _____
3. _____

I'm grateful for…

1. _____
2. _____
3. _____

This is how I'll make today great

_____
_____
_____
_____
_____
_____

Positive affirmation

_____
_____

Enjoy the little things in life because one day you'll look back and realize they were the big things.
KURT VONNEGUT

My good deed today

_____
_____

How I'll improve

_____
_____

Great things I experienced today

1. _____
2. _____
3. _____

5 WEEKLY QUESTIONS

How do you think your best friend or partner would describe you
in one sentence? Now ask them to describe you, and then
compare your assessment with what they said.

What you think:

_____

_____

What they said:

_____

_____

What excites you most about the city or town you live in?

_____

_____

_____

_____

_____

If you could choose any company in the world,
which one would you love to work for most and why?

_____

_____

_____

_____

Is there something that you believe in while others think it's crazy?
What do you think is true even though many people think it isn't?

_____

_____

_____

_____

When was the last time you experienced a few days or a day
without the Internet? What were those days like?

_____

_____

MONTHLY CHECK

Overall Mood:	1	2	3	4	5	6	7	8	9	10
Gratitude:	1	2	3	4	5	6	7	8	9	10
Mindfulness:	1	2	3	4	5	6	7	8	9	10
Family:	1	2	3	4	5	6	7	8	9	10
Friends:	1	2	3	4	5	6	7	8	9	10
Partnership:	1	2	3	4	5	6	7	8	9	10
Having Fun:	1	2	3	4	5	6	7	8	9	10
Calm & Serenity:	1	2	3	4	5	6	7	8	9	10
Time for You:	1	2	3	4	5	6	7	8	9	10
Eating Healthy:	1	2	3	4	5	6	7	8	9	10
Drinking Water:	1	2	3	4	5	6	7	8	9	10
Exercise & Movement:	1	2	3	4	5	6	7	8	9	10
Going Outside:	1	2	3	4	5	6	7	8	9	10
Health:	1	2	3	4	5	6	7	8	9	10
Creativity:	1	2	3	4	5	6	7	8	9	10
Finances:	1	2	3	4	5	6	7	8	9	10
Work & Education:	1	2	3	4	5	6	7	8	9	10
Thoughts & Emotions:	1	2	3	4	5	6	7	8	9	10
The Present:	1	2	3	4	5	6	7	8	9	10
The Future:	1	2	3	4	5	6	7	8	9	10

MONTHLY NOTES

NOTES & IDEAS

_____
_____
_____
_____
_____
_____
_____
_____
_____
_____
_____
_____
_____
_____
_____
_____
_____
_____
_____
_____
_____
_____
_____

HABIT-TRACKER

HABIT	M	T	W	T	F	S	S
	●	●	●	●	●	●	●
	●	●	●	●	●	●	●
	●	●	●	●	●	●	●

I'm grateful for…

1. _____
2. _____
3. _____

This is how I'll make today great

_____
_____
_____
_____
_____

Positive affirmation

_____
_____

Weekly challenge:
This week, treat yourself with the analogue versions of the Internet.
Amazon = go to the shopping centre. Facebook = tell a friend that you like him.
Google = visit a library. Snapchat = pull funny faces in front of the mirror.
Instagram = eat out or exercise. Pay attention to how you feel
afterwards and draw your own conclusions.

My good deed today

_____
_____

How I'll improve

_____
_____

Great things I experienced today

1. _____
2. _____
3. _____

I'm grateful for...

1. _____
2. _____
3. _____

This is how I'll make today great

_____
_____
_____
_____
_____

Positive affirmation

_____
_____

> *We're plugged in 24 hours a day now. We're all part of one big machine, whether we are conscious of that or not. And if we can't unplug from that machine, eventually we're going to become mindless.*
> ALAN LIGHTMAN

My good deed today

_____
_____

How I'll improve

_____
_____

Great things I experienced today

1. _____
2. _____
3. _____

I'm grateful for...

1. _____
2. _____
3. _____

This is how I'll make today great

_____
_____
_____
_____
_____

Positive affirmation

_____
_____

Life isn't about finding yourself.
Life is about creating yourself.
GEORGE BERNARD SHAW

My good deed today

_____
_____

How I'll improve

_____
_____

Great things I experienced today

1. _____
2. _____
3. _____

I'm grateful for…

1. _____
2. _____
3. _____

This is how I'll make today great

_____
_____
_____
_____
_____
_____

Positive affirmation

_____
_____

> *The way to develop the best that is in a person is by appreciation and encouragement.*
>
> CHARLES SCHWAB

My good deed today

_____
_____

How I'll improve

_____
_____

Great things I experienced today

1. _____
2. _____
3. _____

A *GOAL* WITHOUT A **PLAN** IS JUST A WISH "

ANTOINE DE SAINT-EXUPÉRY

•

PLAN YOURSELF HAPPY

UrBestSelf

The 6-Minute Success Journal

**Achieve goals that fulfill your life
– instead of just filling your schedule.**

The combination of positive psychology and mindfulness research enables many of the 700,000 users of *The 6-Minute Diary* to go through life more happily and gratefully. Now, we've merged mindfulness practices and proven strategies for more productivity into a new tool: The *6-Minute Success Journal*. With the help of this book, you'll reach goals with more focus and more calm.

How does it work?

- You reflect your innermost values & needs to set goals you're really passionate about.
- By making prioritisation a priority, you eliminate daily overwhelm and achieve what matters most every day.
- You don't just tick off to-do lists, but also to-relax lists and thereby make sure to cultivate me-time and self-love.
- By transforming your habits, you don't only clear your mind, but also achieve more with less stress.

Follow visions and dreams that would otherwise
be overshadowed by obligations and distractions.

PLAN YOURSELF HAPPY

I'm grateful for...

1. _____
2. _____
3. _____

This is how I'll make today great

_____
_____
_____
_____
_____

Positive affirmation

_____
_____

The weak can never forgive.
Forgiveness is the attribute of the strong.

MAHATMA GANDHI

My good deed today

_____
_____

How I'll improve

_____
_____

Great things I experienced today

1. _____
2. _____
3. _____

I'm grateful for...

1. _____
2. _____
3. _____

This is how I'll make today great

_____
_____
_____
_____
_____

Positive affirmation

_____
_____

If you don't like something, change it.
If you can't change it, change your attitude.
MAYA ANGELOU

My good deed today

_____
_____

How I'll improve

_____
_____

Great things I experienced today

1. _____
2. _____
3. _____

I'm grateful for…

1. _____
2. _____
3. _____

This is how I'll make today great

_____
_____
_____
_____
_____

Positive affirmation

_____
_____

> *The best and most beautiful things in the world cannot be seen or even touched – they must be felt with the heart.*
> HELEN KELLER

My good deed today

_____
_____

How I'll improve

_____
_____

Great things I experienced today

1. _____
2. _____
3. _____

5 WEEKLY QUESTIONS

What are the five top reasons why life is worth living?

_____
_____
_____
_____
_____
_____

How do you say "No" to distractions, invitations and all other activities that do
not match your priorities? How could you improve the way
you say "No" to such things in the future?

_____
_____
_____
_____
_____

In what way are you different from most other people around you?
How do you feel about those differences?

_____
_____
_____
_____
_____

Over the past few years, what did you consider your biggest goals in life?
Were they really your goals or simply what you thought they should be?

_____
_____
_____

When was the last time you lied to somebody and why was that?
In which area of your life are you lying to yourself?

_____
_____
_____

NOTES & IDEAS

_____
_____
_____
_____
_____
_____
_____
_____
_____
_____
_____
_____
_____
_____
_____
_____
_____
_____
_____
_____
_____
_____
_____
_____
_____

HABIT-TRACKER

HABIT	M	T	W	T	F	S	S
	●	●	●	●	●	●	●
	●	●	●	●	●	●	●
	●	●	●	●	●	●	●

I'm grateful for...

1. _____
2. _____
3. _____

This is how I'll make today great

_____
_____
_____
_____
_____

Positive affirmation

_____
_____

Weekly challenge:

In a world of limited time and limitless choices, mastering the tricky art of saying "No" is nothing else than saying "Yes" to your own priorities and needs. This week, alter your language and be honest to yourself and others about what matters most to you: Instead of saying "I'm busy now..." or "I don't have time for...", use "It's not my priority at the moment."

My good deed today

_____
_____

How I'll improve

_____
_____

Great things I experienced today

1. _____
2. _____
3. _____

I'm grateful for…

1. _____
2. _____
3. _____

This is how I'll make today great

_____
_____
_____
_____
_____

Positive affirmation

_____
_____

> *Half of the troubles of this life can be traced to saying yes too quickly and not saying no soon enough.*
>
> JOSH BILLINGS

My good deed today

_____
_____

How I'll improve

_____
_____

Great things I experienced today

1. _____
2. _____
3. _____

I'm grateful for…

1. _____
2. _____
3. _____

This is how I'll make today great

_____
_____
_____
_____
_____

Positive affirmation

_____
_____

You can never leave footprints that last if you are always walking on tiptoe.

LEYMAH GBOWEE

My good deed today

_____
_____

How I'll improve

_____
_____

Great things I experienced today

1. _____
2. _____
3. _____

I'm grateful for…

1. _____
2. _____
3. _____

This is how I'll make today great

_____
_____
_____
_____
_____

Positive affirmation

_____
_____

> *No man ever steps in the same river twice, for it's not the same river and he's not the same man.*
> HERACLITUS

My good deed today

_____
_____

How I'll improve

_____
_____

Great things I experienced today

1. _____
2. _____
3. _____

I'm grateful for...

1. _____
2. _____
3. _____

This is how I'll make today great

_____
_____
_____
_____
_____

Positive affirmation

_____
_____

> **Anything worth having is worth waiting for.**
> SUSAN ELIZABETH PHILLIPS

My good deed today

_____
_____

How I'll improve

_____
_____

Great things I experienced today

1. _____
2. _____
3. _____

I'm grateful for…

1. _____
2. _____
3. _____

This is how I'll make today great

_____
_____
_____
_____
_____

Positive affirmation

_____
_____

> *We must accept finite disappointment,*
> *but we must never lose infinite hope.*
>
> MARTIN LUTHER KING

My good deed today

_____
_____

How I'll improve

_____
_____

Great things I experienced today

1. _____
2. _____
3. _____

I'm grateful for…

1. _____
2. _____
3. _____

This is how I'll make today great

_____
_____
_____
_____
_____

Positive affirmation

_____
_____

> *For every minute you are angry,*
> *you lose sixty seconds of happiness.*
> RALPH WALDO EMERSON

My good deed today

_____
_____

How I'll improve

_____
_____

Great things I experienced today

1. _____
2. _____
3. _____

5 WEEKLY QUESTIONS

Strength or weakness? This is often a question of perspective.
Which of your supposed weaknesses could be a strength and why?

_____

_____

_____

_____

What are your core values? Are you living up to
these values and beliefs in your everyday life?

_____

_____

_____

_____

What motivates you most to get up in the morning? Where does most of your
energy come from? Is there a way to integrate more of that boost into your life?

_____

_____

_____

_____

In your opinion, what is the biggest injustice and why?
How are you contributing to minimising that injustice?

_____

_____

_____

_____

Can you forgive those who have hurt you, leave behind any hard
feelings and move on? When was the last time you actually did that?

_____

_____

_____

_____

NOTES & IDEAS

_____
_____
_____
_____
_____
_____
_____
_____
_____
_____
_____
_____
_____
_____
_____
_____
_____
_____
_____
_____
_____
_____
_____
_____
_____

HABIT-TRACKER

HABIT	M	T	W	T	F	S	S
	●	●	●	●	●	●	●
	●	●	●	●	●	●	●
	●	●	●	●	●	●	●

I'm grateful for…

1. _____
2. _____
3. _____

This is how I'll make today great

_____
_____
_____
_____
_____

Positive affirmation

_____
_____

Weekly challenge:

To forgive and to let go can be as hard as it can be liberating. It takes a load off your shoulders and creates space for new things in your life. As early as 2,500 years ago, Buddha described letting go as the "key to happiness". This week, try to let go and forgive someone. Turn the key and leave your pent-up emotions on the other side of the door.

My good deed today

_____
_____

How I'll improve

_____
_____

Great things I experienced today

1. _____
2. _____
3. _____

I'm grateful for...

1. _____
2. _____
3. _____

This is how I'll make today great

_____
_____
_____
_____
_____

Positive affirmation

_____
_____

> *Any fool can criticize, complain, and condemn*
> *– and most fools do. But it takes character and*
> *self-control to be understanding and forgiving.*
> DALE CARNEGIE

My good deed today

_____
_____

How I'll improve

_____
_____

Great things I experienced today

1. _____
2. _____
3. _____

I'm grateful for...

1. _____
2. _____
3. _____

This is how I'll make today great

_____
_____
_____
_____
_____

Positive affirmation

_____
_____

Things turn out best for people who make the best of the way things turn out.

JOHN WOODEN

My good deed today

_____
_____

How I'll improve

_____
_____

Great things I experienced today

1. _____
2. _____
3. _____

I'm grateful for...

1. _____
2. _____
3. _____

This is how I'll make today great

_____
_____
_____
_____
_____

Positive affirmation

_____
_____

> *Everyone is a genius. But if you judge a fish by its ability to climb a tree, it will live its whole life believing that it is stupid.*
> ALBERT EINSTEIN

My good deed today

_____
_____

How I'll improve

_____
_____

Great things I experienced today

1. _____
2. _____
3. _____

I'm grateful for...

1. _____
2. _____
3. _____

This is how I'll make today great

_____
_____
_____
_____
_____

Positive affirmation

_____
_____

> *Seeking happiness in material things*
> *is a sure way of being unhappy.*
> POPE FRANCIS

My good deed today

_____
_____

How I'll improve

_____
_____

Great things I experienced today

1. _____
2. _____
3. _____

I'm grateful for...

1. _____
2. _____
3. _____

This is how I'll make today great

_____
_____
_____
_____
_____

Positive affirmation

_____
_____

It is not because things are difficult that we do not dare, it is because we do not dare that they are difficult.

LUCIUS ANNAEUS SENECA

My good deed today

_____
_____

How I'll improve

_____
_____

Great things I experienced today

1. _____
2. _____
3. _____

I'm grateful for...

1. _____
2. _____
3. _____

This is how I'll make today great

_____
_____
_____
_____
_____

Positive affirmation

_____
_____

> *Love the life you live. Live the life you love.*
>
> BOB MARLEY

My good deed today

_____
_____

How I'll improve

_____
_____

Great things I experienced today

1. _____
2. _____
3. _____

5 WEEKLY QUESTIONS

What was your last big mistake and what was your all-time favourite one?
What did you learn from them?

_____

_____

_____

_____

_____

If you could experience one day of your life in the exact same way again,
which day would that be? What was so special about that day?

_____

_____

_____

_____

_____

Time for a change of perspective: Is there an outstanding decision, which
you just can't make because you are torn? Surely, you know a person
with whom you don't often agree but whose opinion you value a lot.
What would that person say about your dilemma?

_____

_____

_____

_____

What remains of you if you have to give away
all your belongings and relationships?

_____

_____

_____

_____

What would you rather be: incredibly attractive, an exceptional genius,
a world-famous actor or a billionaire philanthropist? Explain why.

_____

_____

NOTES & IDEAS

_____
_____
_____
_____
_____
_____
_____
_____
_____
_____
_____
_____
_____
_____
_____
_____
_____
_____
_____
_____
_____
_____
_____
_____

HABIT-TRACKER

HABIT	M	T	W	T	F	S	S
	●	●	●	●	●	●	●
	●	●	●	●	●	●	●
	●	●	●	●	●	●	●

I'm grateful for...

1. _____
2. _____
3. _____

This is how I'll make today great

_____
_____
_____
_____
_____

Positive affirmation

_____
_____

Weekly challenge:

If something upsets you this week, revert to a tool that you are always carrying with you: your breath. Focus on breathing in slowly through your nose and then breathing out even slower through your mouth. Identify your emotions instead of identifying with them. It might sound like some esoteric advice but the point is: it actually works and calms you down within seconds.

My good deed today

_____
_____

How I'll improve

_____
_____

Great things I experienced today

1. _____
2. _____
3. _____

MTWTFSS _____

I'm grateful for…

1. _____
2. _____
3. _____

This is how I'll make today great

_____
_____
_____
_____
_____

Positive affirmation

_____
_____

> *When you own your breath,*
> *nobody can steal your peace.*
> ANONYMOUS

My good deed today

_____
_____

How I'll improve

_____
_____

Great things I experienced today

1. _____
2. _____
3. _____

I'm grateful for…

1. _____
2. _____
3. _____

This is how I'll make today great

_____
_____
_____
_____
_____

Positive affirmation

_____
_____

> *Some people are always grumbling because roses have thorns; I am thankful that thorns have roses.*
>
> ALPHONSE KARR

My good deed today

_____
_____

How I'll improve

_____
_____

Great things I experienced today

1. _____
2. _____
3. _____

I'm grateful for…

1. _____
2. _____
3. _____

This is how I'll make today great

_____
_____
_____
_____
_____

Positive affirmation

_____
_____

> *It is important to make a dream of life and of a dream reality.*
> MARIE CURIE

My good deed today

_____
_____

How I'll improve

_____
_____

Great things I experienced today

1. _____
2. _____
3. _____

I'm grateful for...

1. _____
2. _____
3. _____

This is how I'll make today great

_____
_____
_____
_____
_____

Positive affirmation

_____
_____

> *To the world you may just be one person,*
> *but to one person you may be the world.*
> BRANDI SNYDER

My good deed today

_____
_____

How I'll improve

_____
_____

Great things I experienced today

1. _____
2. _____
3. _____

I'm grateful for...

1. _____
2. _____
3. _____

This is how I'll make today great

_____
_____
_____
_____
_____

Positive affirmation

_____
_____

> *If you do what you've always done,*
> *you'll get what you've always gotten.*
> TONY ROBBINS

My good deed today

_____
_____

How I'll improve

_____
_____

Great things I experienced today

1. _____
2. _____
3. _____

I'm grateful for…

1. _____
2. _____
3. _____

This is how I'll make today great

_____
_____
_____
_____
_____
_____

Positive affirmation

_____
_____
_____

> *Be who you are and say what you feel,*
> *because those who mind don't matter*
> *and those who matter don't mind.*
>
> DR. SEUSS

My good deed today

_____
_____

How I'll improve

_____
_____

Great things I experienced today

1. _____
2. _____
3. _____

5 WEEKLY QUESTIONS

Each one of us fulfills different roles in their lives (son, colleague, mother, tenant, best friend, comforter,...). What roles do you fulfill at the moment? Which ones do you like and which ones not so much? Why?

_____

_____

_____

_____

_____

_____

If you had to spend the rest of your life with three people on a deserted island, who would you choose and why?

_____

_____

_____

_____

What was the biggest transformation you have lived through so far and what triggered it?

_____

_____

_____

_____

If you could choose any two people in the present or past to be your mentors/teachers, who would they be and why them?

_____

_____

_____

_____

Do you currently have any obsessions or unusual habits? If yes, how do you feel about them?

_____

_____

_____

MONTHLY CHECK

Overall Mood:	1	2	3	4	5	6	7	8	9	10
Gratitude:	1	2	3	4	5	6	7	8	9	10
Mindfulness:	1	2	3	4	5	6	7	8	9	10
Family:	1	2	3	4	5	6	7	8	9	10
Friends:	1	2	3	4	5	6	7	8	9	10
Partnership:	1	2	3	4	5	6	7	8	9	10
Having Fun:	1	2	3	4	5	6	7	8	9	10
Calm & Serenity:	1	2	3	4	5	6	7	8	9	10
Time for You:	1	2	3	4	5	6	7	8	9	10
Eating Healthy:	1	2	3	4	5	6	7	8	9	10
Drinking Water:	1	2	3	4	5	6	7	8	9	10
Exercise & Movement:	1	2	3	4	5	6	7	8	9	10
Going Outside:	1	2	3	4	5	6	7	8	9	10
Health:	1	2	3	4	5	6	7	8	9	10
Creativity:	1	2	3	4	5	6	7	8	9	10
Finances:	1	2	3	4	5	6	7	8	9	10
Work & Education:	1	2	3	4	5	6	7	8	9	10
Thoughts & Emotions:	1	2	3	4	5	6	7	8	9	10
The Present:	1	2	3	4	5	6	7	8	9	10
The Future:	1	2	3	4	5	6	7	8	9	10

MONTHLY NOTES

NOTES & IDEAS

_____

_____

_____

_____

_____

_____

_____

_____

_____

_____

_____

_____

_____

_____

_____

_____

_____

_____

_____

_____

_____

_____

_____

_____

_____

_____

HABIT-TRACKER

HABIT	M	T	W	T	F	S	S
	●	●	●	●	●	●	●
	●	●	●	●	●	●	●
	●	●	●	●	●	●	●

I'm grateful for...

1. _____
2. _____
3. _____

This is how I'll make today great

_____
_____
_____
_____
_____

Positive affirmation

_____
_____

Weekly challenge:

We all have something that drives us. Encourage someone who has been unmotivated lately by letting them know that you have faith in their abilities. Animate him to pursue his goals and give him the motivational boost he's lacking at the moment.

My good deed today

_____
_____

How I'll improve

_____
_____

Great things I experienced today

1. _____
2. _____
3. _____

I'm grateful for…

1. _____
2. _____
3. _____

This is how I'll make today great

_____
_____
_____
_____
_____

Positive affirmation

_____
_____

> *Treat people as if they were what they ought to be and you help them to become what they are capable of being.*
> JOHANN WOLFGANG VON GOETHE

My good deed today

_____
_____

How I'll improve

_____
_____

Great things I experienced today

1. _____
2. _____
3. _____

I'm grateful for…

1. _____
2. _____
3. _____

This is how I'll make today great

_____
_____
_____
_____
_____

Positive affirmation

_____
_____

You are never too old to set another goal or to dream a new dream.

C. S. LEWIS

My good deed today

_____
_____

How I'll improve

_____
_____

Great things I experienced today

1. _____
2. _____
3. _____

I'm grateful for…

1. _____
2. _____
3. _____

This is how I'll make today great

_____
_____
_____
_____
_____

Positive affirmation

_____
_____

> *Give sorrow words; the grief that does not speak whispers the overwrought heart and bids it break.*
>
> WILLIAM SHAKESPEARE

My good deed today

_____
_____

How I'll improve

_____
_____

Great things I experienced today

1. _____
2. _____
3. _____

I'm grateful for...

1. _____
2. _____
3. _____

This is how I'll make today great

_____
_____
_____
_____
_____

Positive affirmation

_____
_____

To live is the rarest thing in the world.
Most people exist, that is all.
OSCAR WILDE

My good deed today

_____
_____

How I'll improve

_____
_____

Great things I experienced today

1. _____
2. _____
3. _____

I'm grateful for...

1. _____
2. _____
3. _____

This is how I'll make today great

_____
_____
_____
_____
_____

Positive affirmation

_____
_____

> *If you judge people, you have no time to love them.*
> MOTHER TERESA

My good deed today

_____
_____

How I'll improve

_____
_____

Great things I experienced today

1. _____
2. _____
3. _____

I'm grateful for…

1. _____
2. _____
3. _____

This is how I'll make today great

_____
_____
_____
_____
_____

Positive affirmation

_____
_____

> *Stop thinking gratitude is a by-product of your circumstances and start thinking of it as a world view.*
> BRYAN ROBLES

My good deed today

_____
_____

How I'll improve

_____
_____

Great things I experienced today

1. _____
2. _____
3. _____

5 WEEKLY QUESTIONS

Think of a goal you've recently accomplished in your life. What obstacles did you overcome on the way? Why did you set this goal in the first place?

_____

_____

_____

_____

_____

_____

If you could wake up with a new skill tomorrow,
what would that be and why this one in particular?

_____

_____

_____

_____

Which decision was one of the most pivotal ones of your life so far?
How will you approach the next big decision that is currently in the pipeline?

_____

_____

_____

_____

Who have you been thinking about a lot recently? What could this mean?

_____

_____

_____

Are you someone you would like to spend the rest of your life with?
Explain why or why not.

_____

_____

_____

NOTES & IDEAS

_____
_____
_____
_____
_____
_____
_____
_____
_____
_____
_____
_____
_____
_____
_____
_____
_____
_____
_____
_____
_____
_____
_____

HABIT-TRACKER

HABIT	M	T	W	T	F	S	S
	●	●	●	●	●	●	●
	●	●	●	●	●	●	●
	●	●	●	●	●	●	●

I'm grateful for…

1. _____
2. _____
3. _____

This is how I'll make today great

_____
_____
_____
_____
_____

Positive affirmation

_____
_____

Weekly challenge:

No matter how small or grand – a sincere compliment costs nothing, takes no time, and can make someone else's entire day. So get yourself out there and compliment someone this week: Tell the guy at the bus stop how great his jacket looks, let the woman next to you in the cinema know that she's got a contagious laughter or praise the mailman for always being so cheerful.

My good deed today

_____
_____

How I'll improve

_____
_____

Great things I experienced today

1. _____
2. _____
3. _____

I'm grateful for…

1. _____
2. _____
3. _____

This is how I'll make today great

_____
_____
_____
_____
_____

Positive affirmation

_____
_____

> *I can live for two months on a good compliment.*
> MARK TWAIN

My good deed today

_____
_____

How I'll improve

_____
_____

Great things I experienced today

1. _____
2. _____
3. _____

I'm grateful for…

1. _____
2. _____
3. _____

This is how I'll make today great

_____
_____
_____
_____
_____

Positive affirmation

_____
_____

> *Don't be afraid to give up the good to go for the great.*
> JOHN D. ROCKEFELLER

My good deed today

_____
_____

How I'll improve

_____
_____

Great things I experienced today

1. _____
2. _____
3. _____

I'm grateful for…

1. _____
2. _____
3. _____

This is how I'll make today great

_____
_____
_____
_____
_____

Positive affirmation

_____
_____

Health so far outweighs all external goods that a healthy beggar is truly more fortunate than a king in poor health.
ARTHUR SCHOPENHAUER

My good deed today

_____
_____

How I'll improve

_____
_____

Great things I experienced today

1. _____
2. _____
3. _____

I'm grateful for...

1. _____
2. _____
3. _____

This is how I'll make today great

_____
_____
_____
_____
_____

Positive affirmation

_____
_____

> *The freedom of Mankind does not lie in the fact that we can do what we want, but that we do not have to do that which we do not want.*
>
> JEAN JAQUES ROUSSEAU

My good deed today

_____
_____

How I'll improve

_____
_____

Great things I experienced today

1. _____
2. _____
3. _____

I'm grateful for…

1. _____
2. _____
3. _____

This is how I'll make today great

_____
_____
_____
_____
_____

Positive affirmation

_____
_____

> *Everything has beauty, but not everyone sees it.*
> CONFUCIUS

My good deed today

_____
_____

How I'll improve

_____
_____

Great things I experienced today

1. _____
2. _____
3. _____

I'm grateful for...

1. _____
2. _____
3. _____

This is how I'll make today great

_____
_____
_____
_____
_____

Positive affirmation

_____
_____

> *The only man who behaves sensibly is my tailor;*
> *he takes my measure anew each time he sees me.*
> *The rest go on with their old measurements*
> *and expect me to fit them.*
> GEORGE BERNARD SHAW

My good deed today

_____
_____

How I'll improve

_____
_____

Great things I experienced today

1. _____
2. _____
3. _____

5 WEEKLY QUESTIONS

Which behaviours or habits that you adopted over the last few years have significantly improved your life? And how?

_____

_____

_____

_____

_____

_____

Which motto applies best to your life so far? Why is that and do you want your future life to be summarised under the same motto?

_____

_____

_____

_____

_____

If you could snap your fingers and achieve a goal in your personal life, what would it be? What is one very small step you can take right now to get the ball rolling?

_____

_____

_____

_____

If you asked your parents, your partner or your best friend what you can do best, what would they say?

_____

_____

_____

Whom did you last find very attractive and what was so appealing about that person? What characteristics do you generally find most attractive in a person?

_____

_____

_____

NOTES & IDEAS

HABIT-TRACKER

HABIT	M	T	W	T	F	S	S
	●	●	●	●	●	●	●
	●	●	●	●	●	●	●
	●	●	●	●	●	●	●

I'm grateful for…

1. _____
2. _____
3. _____

This is how I'll make today great

_____
_____
_____
_____
_____

Positive affirmation

_____
_____

Weekly challenge:

Studies show that millions of grey cells only get activated when you switch off and aren't doing a particular task.[63] Take a few minutes to slow down during a busy day: breathe, disconnect, let your mind wander and your phantasy run free. Brain researchers found that this helps you become up to 41% more creative and productive during the work phases that follow.[64]

My good deed today

_____
_____

How I'll improve

_____
_____

Great things I experienced today

1. _____
2. _____
3. _____

I'm grateful for…

1. _____
2. _____
3. _____

This is how I'll make today great

_____
_____
_____
_____
_____

Positive affirmation

_____
_____

> *In this media-drenched, multitasking and always-on age, many of us have forgotten how to unplug and immerse ourselves completely in the moment. We have forgotten how to slow down.*
>
> CARL HONORÉ

My good deed today

_____
_____

How I'll improve

_____
_____

Great things I experienced today

1. _____
2. _____
3. _____

I'm grateful for...

1. _____
2. _____
3. _____

This is how I'll make today great

_____
_____
_____
_____
_____

Positive affirmation

_____
_____

*You don't learn to walk by following rules.
You learn by doing, and by falling over.*
RICHARD BRANSON

My good deed today

_____
_____

How I'll improve

_____
_____

Great things I experienced today

1. _____
2. _____
3. _____

I'm grateful for…

1. _____
2. _____
3. _____

This is how I'll make today great

_____
_____
_____
_____
_____

Positive affirmation

_____
_____

> *The world breaks everyone, and afterward,*
> *many are strong at the broken places.*
> ERNEST HEMINGWAY

My good deed today

_____
_____

How I'll improve

_____
_____

Great things I experienced today

1. _____
2. _____
3. _____

I'm grateful for…

1. _____
2. _____
3. _____

This is how I'll make today great

_____
_____
_____
_____
_____

Positive affirmation

_____
_____

Even the stones placed in one's path can be made into something beautiful.

JOHANN WOLFGANG VON GOETHE

My good deed today

_____
_____

How I'll improve

_____
_____

Great things I experienced today

1. _____
2. _____
3. _____

I'm grateful for…

1. _____

2. _____

3. _____

This is how I'll make today great

_____

_____

_____

_____

_____

Positive affirmation

_____

_____

Only those who will risk going too far can possibly find out how far one can go.

T.S. ELIOT

My good deed today

_____

_____

How I'll improve

_____

_____

Great things I experienced today

1. _____

2. _____

3. _____

I'm grateful for...

1. _____
2. _____
3. _____

This is how I'll make today great

_____
_____
_____
_____
_____

Positive affirmation

_____
_____

> *The only limit to our realization of tomorrow will be our doubts of today.*
> FRANKLIN D. ROOSEVELT

My good deed today

_____
_____

How I'll improve

_____
_____

Great things I experienced today

1. _____
2. _____
3. _____

5 WEEKLY QUESTIONS

What was the best holiday of your life and why was it so unique?

_____

_____

_____

_____

_____

_____

Who has had the greatest influence on your life and how exactly did this person influence you? Who do you think is the person you have influenced the most?

_____

_____

_____

_____

_____

What is your earliest and what is your best childhood memory?
If you picture yourself as a child now, what are you doing?

_____

_____

_____

_____

_____

Which movie could you watch over and over? What book could you read several times? And what could your answers possibly reveal about you?

_____

_____

_____

_____

What do you think are the best things about getting older?

_____

_____

_____

NOTES & IDEAS

_____
_____
_____
_____
_____
_____
_____
_____
_____
_____
_____
_____
_____
_____
_____
_____
_____
_____
_____
_____
_____
_____
_____
_____

HABIT-TRACKER

HABIT	M	T	W	T	F	S	S
	●	●	●	●	●	●	●
	●	●	●	●	●	●	●
	●	●	●	●	●	●	●

MTWTFSS _____

I'm grateful for...

1. _____
2. _____
3. _____

This is how I'll make today great

_____
_____
_____
_____
_____

Positive affirmation

_____
_____

Weekly challenge:

Why is it that we always need an occasion to let our loved ones know
how much they mean to us? This week, swim against the tide and write a
nice note for somebody you want to surprise. It's not the content but the
thought that counts: let the recipient know that you thought of him/her.
PS: Why not hide your little message in his/her pocket or purse?

My good deed today

_____
_____

How I'll improve

_____
_____

Great things I experienced today

1. _____
2. _____
3. _____

I'm grateful for...

1. _____
2. _____
3. _____

This is how I'll make today great

_____
_____
_____
_____
_____

Positive affirmation

_____
_____

Our fingerprints don't fade from the lives we've touched.
ROBERT PATTINSON

My good deed today

_____
_____

How I'll improve

_____
_____

Great things I experienced today

1. _____
2. _____
3. _____

I'm grateful for…

1. _____
2. _____
3. _____

This is how I'll make today great

_____
_____
_____
_____
_____

Positive affirmation

_____
_____

It is not necessary to do extraordinary things to get extraordinary results.

WARREN BUFFET

My good deed today

_____
_____

How I'll improve

_____
_____

Great things I experienced today

1. _____
2. _____
3. _____

I'm grateful for…

1. _____
2. _____
3. _____

This is how I'll make today great

_____
_____
_____
_____
_____

Positive affirmation

_____
_____

> *Don't choose the one who is beautiful
> in the world, but rather choose the one
> who makes your world beautiful.*
> ALICE SEBOLD

My good deed today

_____
_____

How I'll improve

_____
_____

Great things I experienced today

1. _____
2. _____
3. _____

I'm grateful for...

1. _____
2. _____
3. _____

This is how I'll make today great

_____
_____
_____
_____
_____

Positive affirmation

_____
_____

> *If we are so busy being successful that we don't have time to be happy, then we need to seriously reconsider our definition of success.*
>
> MARIA POPOVA

My good deed today

_____
_____

How I'll improve

_____
_____

Great things I experienced today

1. _____
2. _____
3. _____

I'm grateful for…

1. _____
2. _____
3. _____

This is how I'll make today great

_____
_____
_____
_____
_____

Positive affirmation

_____
_____

> *I cannot say whether things will get better if we change; what I can say is that they must change if they are to get better.*
> GEORG CHRISTOPH LICHTENBERG

My good deed today

_____
_____

How I'll improve

_____
_____

Great things I experienced today

1. _____
2. _____
3. _____

I'm grateful for...

1. _____
2. _____
3. _____

This is how I'll make today great

_____
_____
_____
_____
_____

Positive affirmation

_____
_____

> *You give little when you give your possessions.*
> *It is when you give of yourself that you truly give.*
> KHALIL GIBRAN

My good deed today

_____
_____

How I'll improve

_____
_____

Great things I experienced today

1. _____
2. _____
3. _____

5 WEEKLY QUESTIONS

What was the hardest time of your life? What helped you
get through it and how did you grow from that experience?

_____

_____

_____

_____

_____

_____

What kind of person are you when you are by yourself?
What do you like to do when you're alone?

_____

_____

_____

_____

_____

How did your parents raise you? What would you (or do you)
do similarly/differently with your own children?

_____

_____

_____

In which situations do you feel most like yourself?
Are there situations in which you behave inauthentically?

_____

_____

Smile time: When did you have your last intense outburst of laughter?
What made you smile most this week?

_____

_____

MONTHLY CHECK

Overall Mood:	1	2	3	4	5	6	7	8	9	10
Gratitude:	1	2	3	4	5	6	7	8	9	10
Mindfulness:	1	2	3	4	5	6	7	8	9	10
Family:	1	2	3	4	5	6	7	8	9	10
Friends:	1	2	3	4	5	6	7	8	9	10
Partnership:	1	2	3	4	5	6	7	8	9	10
Having Fun:	1	2	3	4	5	6	7	8	9	10
Calm & Serenity:	1	2	3	4	5	6	7	8	9	10
Time for You:	1	2	3	4	5	6	7	8	9	10
Eating Healthy:	1	2	3	4	5	6	7	8	9	10
Drinking Water:	1	2	3	4	5	6	7	8	9	10
Exercise & Movement:	1	2	3	4	5	6	7	8	9	10
Going Outside:	1	2	3	4	5	6	7	8	9	10
Health:	1	2	3	4	5	6	7	8	9	10
Creativity:	1	2	3	4	5	6	7	8	9	10
Finances:	1	2	3	4	5	6	7	8	9	10
Work & Education:	1	2	3	4	5	6	7	8	9	10
Thoughts & Emotions:	1	2	3	4	5	6	7	8	9	10
The Present:	1	2	3	4	5	6	7	8	9	10
The Future:	1	2	3	4	5	6	7	8	9	10

MONTHLY NOTES

_____

_____

_____

_____

_____

_____

_____

_____

NOTES & IDEAS

HABIT-TRACKER

HABIT	M	T	W	T	F	S	S
	○	○	○	○	○	○	○
	○	○	○	○	○	○	○
	○	○	○	○	○	○	○

A friendly
Reminder
… only two weeks left.

The 6-Minute Diary can only accompany you for another two weeks. Have you enjoyed the journey so far? If so, then it's time to continue your daily happiness journey. Visit our website createurbestself.com and treat yourself to the next travel companion:

This follow-up version comes with a new weekly routine, brand-new weekly challenges and spanking new daily quotes. It will boost your happiness for another six months, so that together with your *6-Minute Diary*, you will capture an entire year of becoming *UrBestSelf*.

At this point of your journey, desirable habits like gratitude, mindfulness and growth through daily reflection have most probably become habitual for you. But what about unwanted habits once they are no longer part of your life? Do they just disappear? Unfortunately not, because contrary to what one might assume, the neural pathways of these undesirable habits never really disappear. In fact, ingrained habits – no matter if old or new – are actual tangible structures in our body. These structures are located in the area of our brain where habit formation takes place: the so-called basal ganglia. Once a habit is entrenched in your life, it is also cemented into your brain's neural pathways.[66] Therefore, the neurological structures of old bad habits remain ingrained in our brains, ready to be reactivated as soon as we lose our focus on the maintenance of our newly acquired positive habits.[67]

Since past behaviours are always just around the corner – on the cusp of being reactivated, you have to ensure you won't fall back into old patterns. Stick to your daily, weekly and monthly routine and make positive changes part of your everyday life. Make sure to make gratitude your attitude and go through your day with less stress and more mindfulness.

I'm grateful for…

1. _____
2. _____
3. _____

This is how I'll make today great

_____
_____
_____
_____
_____

Positive affirmation

_____
_____

Weekly challenge:

Studies reveal that we are much better at detecting other people's faults than our own.[65] Even though you have formed a firm opinion about yourself, an outside perspective can provide new impulses and valuable food for thought. So whose opinion do you value? Ask that person how he thinks you could improve.
At worst, you might learn something new about yourself :)

My good deed today

_____
_____

How I'll improve

_____
_____

Great things I experienced today

1. _____
2. _____
3. _____

WHAT YOU DO
TODAY
can improve
all your
TOMORROWS

UrBestSelf

THANK YOU!

At *UrBestSelf*, we create books that guide you to find your very own way of becoming your best self. We are grateful that you have welcomed one of these books into its new home!

Action may not always bring happiness,
but there is no happiness without action.

WILLIAM JAMES

Once you open *The 6-Minute Diary*, proactive action becomes a habit and your personal journey towards a more fulfilling life begins. Your daily *6-Minute Routine* will help you create a life that you really love by making positive changes part of your everyday life. So put your personal fingerprint on this book and turn your vision into reality:

Make gratitude your attitude and go through your day
with less stress and more mindfulness!

To get the most out of your *6-Minute Diary*, we have prepared some extra candies for you.

» eBook: *The Golden Morning Routine* – the science behind morning routines rounded up with 25 examples of successful people

» A preview to the eBook *The Golden Evening Routine* which comes in full length with the follow-up version: *The 6-Minute Diary Pure*

Just visit: *createurbestself.com/stayontheball*

Come aboard and let the diary take full effect on your life.

Are you happy with *The 6-Minute Diary*?

Why not collect some karma points and help others to come on-board a unique happiness journey? Just leave a review on Amazon – even if it's just one sentence – we would be more than grateful! Of course you can also share a personal message with us anytime: *hello@createurbestself.com* :)

Your *UrBestSelf*-Team

Everything you want to be is already inside you!

I'm grateful for…

1. _____
2. _____
3. _____

This is how I'll make today great

_____
_____
_____
_____
_____
_____

Positive affirmation

_____
_____
_____

*Though you see the 7 mistakes of others,
you do not see your own 10 mistakes.*
JAPANESE PROVERB

My good deed today

_____
_____

How I'll improve

_____
_____

Great things I experienced today

1. _____
2. _____
3. _____

I'm grateful for...

1. _____
2. _____
3. _____

This is how I'll make today great

_____
_____
_____
_____
_____

Positive affirmation

_____
_____

> *Happiness is a state of inner fulfillment, not the gratification of inexhaustible desires for outward things.*
> MATTHIEU RICARD

My good deed today

_____
_____

How I'll improve

_____
_____

Great things I experienced today

1. _____
2. _____
3. _____

I'm grateful for…

1. _____
2. _____
3. _____

This is how I'll make today great

_____
_____
_____
_____
_____

Positive affirmation

_____
_____

> *It has been my experience that folks*
> *who have no vices have very few virtues.*
> ABRAHAM LINCOLN

My good deed today

_____
_____

How I'll improve

_____
_____

Great things I experienced today

1. _____
2. _____
3. _____

I'm grateful for...

1. _____
2. _____
3. _____

This is how I'll make today great

_____
_____
_____
_____
_____

Positive affirmation

_____
_____

If you're brave enough to say goodbye, life will reward you with a new hello.
PAULO COELHO

My good deed today

_____
_____

How I'll improve

_____
_____

Great things I experienced today

1. _____
2. _____
3. _____

I'm grateful for…

1. _____
2. _____
3. _____

This is how I'll make today great

_____
_____
_____
_____
_____

Positive affirmation

_____
_____

Some people feel the rain. Others just get wet.

BOB MARLEY

My good deed today

_____
_____

How I'll improve

_____
_____

Great things I experienced today

1. _____
2. _____
3. _____

I'm grateful for…

1. _____
2. _____
3. _____

This is how I'll make today great

_____
_____
_____
_____
_____

Positive affirmation

_____
_____

If you think you're too small to have an impact, try going to bed with a mosquito in the room.

ANITA RODDICK

My good deed today

_____
_____

How I'll improve

_____
_____

Great things I experienced today

1. _____
2. _____
3. _____

5 WEEKLY QUESTIONS

What did you use to be worried about a few years ago?
Do any of those things matter at all today? What has changed?

_____

_____

_____

_____

_____

What do you value most in a friendship?
To what extent do you live those values yourself?

_____

_____

_____

_____

_____

When was the last time you relied purely on your gut feeling?
How did that make you feel and what was the outcome of your decision?

_____

_____

_____

_____

Who do you love and in what way are you fully present when you're
with them? How are you showing your love to your beloved ones?

_____

_____

_____

_____

What is the most thoughtful gift you've ever received?
What do you think is the best gift you have ever given to someone?

_____

_____

_____

NOTES & IDEAS

_____
_____
_____
_____
_____
_____
_____
_____
_____
_____
_____
_____
_____
_____
_____
_____
_____
_____
_____
_____
_____
_____
_____

HABIT-TRACKER

HABIT	M	T	W	T	F	S	S
	●	●	●	●	●	●	●
	●	●	●	●	●	●	●
	●	●	●	●	●	●	●

I'm grateful for…

1. _____
2. _____
3. _____

This is how I'll make today great

_____
_____
_____
_____
_____

Positive affirmation

_____
_____

Weekly challenge:

"How are you doing", "How is it going?" These questions –
just like the responses to them – have degenerated into empty phrases.
If you're really interested in a genuine response and in hearing more than
a robotic "Fine, and you?", just ask: "What's on your mind currently?".
Watch how such a small alteration can make a huge difference.

My good deed today

_____
_____

How I'll improve

_____
_____

Great things I experienced today

1. _____
2. _____
3. _____

I'm grateful for…

1. _____
2. _____
3. _____

This is how I'll make today great

_____
_____
_____
_____
_____

Positive affirmation

_____
_____

"

By changing nothing, nothing changes.

TONY ROBBINS

"

My good deed today

_____
_____

How I'll improve

_____
_____

Great things I experienced today

1. _____
2. _____
3. _____

I'm grateful for...

1. _____
2. _____
3. _____

This is how I'll make today great

_____
_____
_____
_____
_____

Positive affirmation

_____
_____

> *The art of being happy lies in the power of extracting happiness from common things.*
>
> HENRY WARD BEECHER

My good deed today

_____
_____

How I'll improve

_____
_____

Great things I experienced today

1. _____
2. _____
3. _____

I'm grateful for...

1. _____
2. _____
3. _____

This is how I'll make today great

_____
_____
_____
_____
_____

Positive affirmation

_____
_____

If you really look closely, most overnight successes took a really long time.
STEVE JOBS

My good deed today

_____
_____

How I'll improve

_____
_____

Great things I experienced today

1. _____
2. _____
3. _____

I'm grateful for…

1. _____
2. _____
3. _____

This is how I'll make today great

_____
_____
_____
_____
_____

Positive affirmation

_____
_____

> *No one should be ashamed to admit they
> are wrong, which is but saying, in other words,
> that they are wiser today than they were yesterday.*
> ALEXANDER POPE

My good deed today

_____
_____

How I'll improve

_____
_____

Great things I experienced today

1. _____
2. _____
3. _____

I'm grateful for…

1. _____
2. _____
3. _____

This is how I'll make today great

_____
_____
_____
_____
_____

Positive affirmation

_____
_____

> *Think of what you have rather than of what you lack. Of the things you have, select the best and then reflect how eagerly you would have sought them if you did not have them.*
> MARCUS AURELIUS

My good deed today

_____
_____

How I'll improve

_____
_____

Great things I experienced today

1. _____
2. _____
3. _____

I'm grateful for...

1. _____
2. _____
3. _____

This is how I'll make today great

_____
_____
_____
_____
_____
_____

Positive affirmation

_____
_____

> *A great attitude becomes a great day*
> *which becomes a great month which becomes*
> *a great year which becomes a great life.*
> MANDY HALE

My good deed today

_____
_____

How I'll improve

_____
_____

Great things I experienced today

1. _____
2. _____
3. _____

5 WEEKLY QUESTIONS

How could you be kinder to yourself?

_____

_____

_____

_____

_____

_____

What would you do with your time if you couldn't enter your home from
8am – 7pm, didn't have to work, and your children were being taken care of?

_____

_____

_____

_____

When was the last time you did something
for the first time? How did that make you feel?

_____

_____

_____

_____

If you could direct a movie based on your life, what would be the plot
in one sentence? Who would play you and why this person in particular?

_____

_____

_____

_____

What are the two most beautiful thoughts you can possibly have right now?

_____

_____

_____

_____

FINAL CHECK

Overall Mood:	1	2	3	4	5	6	7	8	9	10
Gratitude:	1	2	3	4	5	6	7	8	9	10
Mindfulness:	1	2	3	4	5	6	7	8	9	10
Family:	1	2	3	4	5	6	7	8	9	10
Friends:	1	2	3	4	5	6	7	8	9	10
Partnership:	1	2	3	4	5	6	7	8	9	10
Having Fun:	1	2	3	4	5	6	7	8	9	10
Calm & Serenity:	1	2	3	4	5	6	7	8	9	10
Time for You:	1	2	3	4	5	6	7	8	9	10
Eating Healthy:	1	2	3	4	5	6	7	8	9	10
Drinking Water:	1	2	3	4	5	6	7	8	9	10
Exercise & Movement:	1	2	3	4	5	6	7	8	9	10
Going Outside:	1	2	3	4	5	6	7	8	9	10
Health:	1	2	3	4	5	6	7	8	9	10
Creativity:	1	2	3	4	5	6	7	8	9	10
Finances:	1	2	3	4	5	6	7	8	9	10
Work & Education:	1	2	3	4	5	6	7	8	9	10
Thoughts & Emotions:	1	2	3	4	5	6	7	8	9	10
The Present:	1	2	3	4	5	6	7	8	9	10
The Future:	1	2	3	4	5	6	7	8	9	10

FINAL NOTES

_____

_____

_____

_____

_____

_____

_____

_____

_____

_____

A huge
Milestone
… you made it!

You deserve a pat on the back and have every reason to be proud of yourself because you've just completed your first *6-Minute Diary*! How do you feel right now? You're more than entitled to feel great and grandiose…

Take a few minutes to leaf through the book. Inhale satisfaction and exhale doubt. Treat yourself to something special and appreciate how much you have achieved to draw energy for future goals and challenges from it. Don't forget to actually cherish what you've accomplished! Enjoy what you have done and let your success sink in…

Now, take a look at all your monthly checks and reflect on your journey of positive changes. What did you learn about yourself, and when did you feel the strongest sense of achievement? What attitudes and behaviours have you changed since using the Diary?

Last but not least, we have a little question for you: What was your good deed today? Your answer: I wrote a review about my experiences with *The 6-Minute Diary* :)

Even if it's just one sentence, this little favour would be of immense value to our little publishing house. Recent reviews on *Amazon* allow us to appear in search results and help people find us easier. This way, we can continue developing books that spread more gratitude, mindfulness and self-love. Thank you for your support.

Of course you can also share a personal message with us anytime…

Get in touch on: createurbestself.com
or via Instagram: @createurbestself

UrBestSelf

How about

... more food for thought?

If you enjoyed *The 6-Minute Diary*,
you might also love our newsletter, *The Mindful Three*.

Every other week, *The Mindful Three* will appear in your inbox with three evidence-based and practical impulses for more mindfulness, less stress and more happiness. These can be inspiring real life stories, brand new articles, exclusive promotional offers or the latest research findings that we've turned into practical tips. We also regularly recommend non-fiction books that we consider worth reading and that have positively influenced our lives – we hope you'll find them just as helpful.

Sounds good?
Then go ahead and sign up for our free newsletter:
createurbestself.com

Dominik & the *UrBestSelf*-Team

We're looking forward to inspiring you!

"

There are only two ways to live your life.
One is as though nothing is a miracle.
The other is as though everything is a miracle.
ALBERT EINSTEIN

The Mindful Three: Bi-weekly inspiration delivered to your inbox.

NOTES & IDEAS

NOTES & IDEAS

NOTES & IDEAS

NOTES & IDEAS

References

1. The software that governs our brain
The Tim Ferriss Show: On Achievement Versus Fulfillment, 178th Episode

2. You learn more quickly from bad experiences than from good ones
Hanson, Rick (2016): Hardwiring Happiness. The New Brain Science of Contentment, Calm and Confidence

3. Angry faces are identified much faster than happy ones
Fox, Elaine / Leser, Victoria / Russo, Ricardo/ Bowles, R.J. / Pichler, Alessio / Dutton, Kevin (2000): Facial Expressions of Emotion. Are Angry Faces Detected More Efficiently?, in: Cognition and Emotion 14 (1)

4. Our brain reacts more quickly to bad things than to good things
Haidt, Jonathan (2009): The Happiness Hypothesis. Putting Ancient Wisdom and Philosophy to the Test of Modern Science

5. The pain of loss is stronger than the joy of possessing the same thing
Baumeister, Roy F. / Bratslavsky, Ellen / Finkenauer, Catrin / Vohs, Kathleen D. (2001): Bad Is Stronger Than Good, in: Review of General Psychology, 5th Edition (4)

6. The joy of gaining money vs. the pain of losing that same amount
Kahneman, D. / Tversky, A. (1979): Prospect Theory. An analysis of decisions under risk, in: Econometrica 47

7. Five good actions to make up for the damage of one bad action
Gottman, J. (1994): Why Marriages Succeed or Fail. And How You Can Make Yours Last

8. 66 days to form a new habit
Lally, Phillippa / H. M. Van Jaarsveld, Cornelia / Potts, Henry W. W. / Wardle, Jane (2009): How habits are formed. Modelling habit formation in the real world, in: European Journal of Social Psychology, 40th Edition (6)

9. Almost everybody fails in achieving her/his goals
Sarner, Moya (2017): 'Anyone can change any habit': the science of keeping your 2018 resolutions.
https://www.theguardian.com/lifeandstyle/2017/dec/29/anyone-can-change-any-habit-science-keeping-2018-resolutions

10. The pen is mightier than the keyboard
Mueller, Pam A. / Oppenheimer, Daniel M. (2014): The Pen is Mightier Than the Keyboard. Advantages of Longhand Over Laptop Note Taking, in: Psychological Science, 25th Edition (6)

11. The link between handwriting and wound healing
Koschwanez, Heide E. / Kerse, Ngaire / Darragh Margot / Jarret Paul / Booth Roger J. / Broadbent Elizabeth (2013): Expressive writing and wound healing in older adults. A randomized controlled trial, in: Psychosomatic Medicine, 78th Edition (6)

12. Naval Ravikant's important life lesson
The Tim Ferriss Show: Naval Ravikant on Happiness Hacks and the 5 Chimps Theory, 136th Episode

13. External circumstances don't make you happy in the long run
Lama, Dalai (2009): The Art of Happiness. A Handbook for Living

14. Quote by Ray Dalio
Dalio, Ray (2017). Principles. Life and Work.

15. Quote by Tim Ferriss
Ferriss, Tim (2009): The 4-Hour Workweek. Escape 9-5, Live Anywhere, and Join the New Rich.

16. Most people consider themselves as "quite happy"
Myers, David G. (2000): The Funds, Friends, and Faith of Happy People, in: American Psychologist, 55th Edition (1)

17. Suppressed emotions become even worse
Garland, Eric, L. / Carter, Kristin / Ropes, Katie / Howard, Matthew O. (2011): Thought Suppression, Impaired Regulation of Urges, and Addiction-Stroop Predict Affect-Modulated Cue-Reactivity among Alcohol Dependent Adults, in: Biological Psychology, 89th Edition (1)

18. Only 5% of our decisions are made consciously
Zaltmann, Gerald (2003): How Customers Think: Essential Insights into the Mind of the Market

19. 40% of our behaviour is repeated daily
Wood, Wendy / Quinn, Jeffrey M. / Kashy, Deborah A. (2002): Habits in Everyday Life: Thought, Emotion and Action, in: Journal of Personality and Social Psychology, 83rd Edition (6)

20. The daily willpower is a limited resource
Hagger, Martin S. / Wood, Chantelle / Stiff, Chris / Nikos, L. D. / (2014): Ego Depletion and the Strength Model of Self-Control. A Meta-Analysis, in: Psychological Bulletin, 136th Edition (4)

21. see source 7

22. Brain areas can be trained like muscles
Maguire, Eleanor A. / Spiers, Hugo J. / Woollett, Katherine (2006): London Taxi Drivers. A Structural MRI and Neuropsychological Analysis, in: Hippocampus, 16th Edition (12)

23. The importance of keystone habits
Duhigg, Charles (2014): The Power of Habit: Why We Do What We Do in Life and Business

24. Study on the effects of lifting weights for two months
Baumeister, Roy F. et al. (2006). "Self-Regulation and Personality. How Interventions Increase Regulatory Success, and How Depletion Moderates the Effects of Traits in Behaviour", in: Journal of Personality 74: 1773-1801

25. Study on financial monitoring and its effects
Oaten, Megan / Cheng K. (2007): "Improvements in Self-Control from Financial Monitoring", in: Journal of Economic Psychology 28: 487-501

26. What is self-reflection?
Law, Lai Chong / Mandl, Heinz / Henninger, Michael (1998): Training of Reflection. Its feasibility and boundary conditions, in: Institut für pädagogische Psychologie und empirische Pädagogik

27. The numerous advantages of sophisticated self-reflection
Schaw, Gregory (1998): Promoting general metacognitive awareness, in: Instructional Science, 26th Edition

28. Adding or removing key details without realising it
Gilbert, Daniel (2007): Stumbling on Happiness

29. 78% look on their mobile phone in the first 15 minutes of the day
Lee, Paul / Calugar-Pop, Cornelia (2015): Global Mobile Consumer Survey. Insights into global consumer mobile trends. http://www2.deloitte.com/global/en/pages/technology-media-and-telecommunications/articles/global-mobile-consumer-survey.html

30. Women in Japan get approximately 87 years old
WHO-Report (2014): World Health Statistics 2014. Large gains in Life Expectancy. http://www.who.int/mediacentre/news/releases/2014/world-health-statistics-2014/en/

31. Remarkable long-term effects of gratitude
Emmons, Robert A. / McCullough, Michael E. (2003): Counting Blessings Versus Burdens. An Experimental Investigation of Gratitude and Subjective Well-Being in Daily Life, in: Journal of Personality and Social Psychology, 84th Edition (2)

32. Gratitude may help you live longer
Kalokerinos, E.K. / von Hippel, W. / Henry, J. D. / Trivers, R. (2014). The aging positivity effect and immune function: Positivity in recall predicts higher CD4 counts and lower CD4 activation. Psychology and Aging, 29(3), 636-641

33. Oprah Winfrey on her gratitude diary
Oprah Winfrey Network, OWN (2012): Oprah's Gratitude Journal. Oprah's Life Class. Oprah Life Lessons, https://www.youtube.com/watch?v=JzFiKRpsz8c, (0.06 – 0.39 min)

34. One of many evidences that the diary works
Seligman, Martin E. P. / Steen, Tracy A. / Park, Nansook / Peterson, Christopher (2005): Positive Psychology Progress. Empirical Validation of Interventions, in: American Psychologist, 60th Edition (5)

35. Gratitude fosters success, not the other way around
Achor, S.: Happiness Advantage (2011): The Seven Principles That Fuel Success and Performance at Work

36. The difference between positive and bad thinking
Carnegie, Dale (1990): How To Stop Worrying and Start Living

37. Healthy optimism improves and extends your life
Seligman, Martin E. P. (2004): Authentic Happiness. Using the New Positive Psychology to Realise Your Potential for Lasting Fulfillment

38. Tony Robbins on his morning ritual
Oprah Winfrey Network, OWN (2016): Tony Robbins' 10-Minute Morning Ritual. SuperSoul Sunday. Oprah Winfrey Network, https://www.youtube.com/watch?v=cgnu9mapQiQ, (1.04 – 1.18 min)

39. The impact of gratitude on your relationships
Watkins, Philip C. (2014): Gratitude and the Good Life. Toward a Psychology of Appreciation

40. Relationships and their impact on the personal well-being
Diener, Ed / Seligman, Martin E. P. (2002): Research Report. Very Happy People, in: Psychological Science, 13th Edition (1)

41. A good posture makes you more attractive
Mehrabian, Albert / Blum, Jeffrey S. (1997): Physical appearance, attractiveness, and the mediating role of emotions, in: Current Psychology. A Journal for Diverse Perspectives on Diverse Psychological Issues, 16th Edition (1)

42. Conscious vs. subconscious information processing in your brain
Dispenza, Joe (2008): Evolve your Brain. The Science of Changing Your Mind

43. The principles of selective perception
Eccles, John C. (1996): How the Self controls its Brain

44. The happy brain is more productive and creative
Achor, Shawn (2012): Positive Intelligence, in: Harvard Business Review, 1st Edition

45. see source 15

46. Affirmations help to reprogram the subconscious mind
N. Cascio, Christopher / Brook O'Donnel, Matthew / Falk, Emily B. / Taylor, Shelley E. / Tinney, Francis J. (2015) Self-affirmation activates brain systems associated with self-related processing and reward and is reinforced by future orientation, in: Social Cognitive and Affective Neuroscience, 11th Edition (4)

47. Negative und negated affirmations
Baumann, Siguard (2006): Psychologie im Sport

48. Using the mobile phone in the last five minutes of the day
Lee, Paul / Calugar-Pop, Cornelia (2015): Global Mobile Consumer Survey. Insights into global consumer mobile trends. http://www2.deloitte.com/global/en/pages/technology-media-and-telecommunications/articles/global-mobile-consumer-survey.html

49. Negative effects of electronic devices before bedtime
Eggermont, Steven / Van den Bulck, Jan (2006): Nodding off or switching off? The use of popular media as a sleep aid in the secondary-school children, in: Journal of Paediatrics and Child Health, 30th Edition (9)

50. The light from electronic devices promotes wakefulness

Lewis, Tanya (2015): Here's what happened when I stopped looking at screens at night.
http://uk.businessinsider.com/why-its-bad-to-use-your-phone-before-bed-2015-7?r=US&IR=T

51. Prosocial people tend to be happier

Lyubomirsky, Sonja / King, Laura / Diener, Ed (2005): The Benefits of Frequent Positive Affect.Does Happiness Lead to Success?, in: Psychological Bulletin, 131st Edition (6)

52. Doing something good for others makes happy in the long term

Svoboda, Elizabeth (2013): What makes a hero?: The Surprising Science of Selflessness

53. The feeling of happiness after giving lasts relatively longer

Seligman, Martin E. P. (2006): Learned Optimism. How to Change Your Mind and Your Life

54. Negative effects of constantly comparing yourself to others

Swallow, Stephen R. / Kuiper, Nicholas A.: Social Comparison and negative self-evaluations. An application to depression, in: Clinical Pschology Review, 8th Edition (1)

55. A positive attitude increases life expectancy

Danner, D. Danner / Snowdon, David A. / Friesen, Wallace V. (2013): Positive Emotions in Early Life and Longevity. Findings from the Study, in: Journal of Personality and Social Pschology, 80th Edition (5)

56. How positive experiences can be transferred to long-term memory

Hanson, Rick (2016): Hardwiring Happiness. The New Brain Science of Contentment, Calm and Confidence

57. The power of visual processing

Merieb, E. N. & Hoehn, K. (2007). Human Anatomy & Physiology 7th Edition, Pearson International Edition

58. Positive effects of gentle pressure by friends and family

Hayes, Stephen C. / Rosenfarb, Irwin / Wulfert, Edelgard / Mund, Edwin D. / Korn, Zamir / Zettle, Robert D. (1985): Self-reinforcement effects. An artifact of social standard setting?, in: Journal of Applied Behaviour Analysis, 18th Edition (3)

59. 85% of our worries have a positive outcome

Robert L. Leahy (2011): Are you a worrier? 5 Tips to turn worry on its head.
https://www.huffingtonpost.com/robert-leahy-phd/how-to-stop-worrying-_b_825063.html

60. We judge about 35,000 times a day

Hoomans, Joel (2015): 35,000 Decisions. The Great Choices of Strategic Leaders.
https://go.roberts.edu/leadingedge/the-great-choices-of-strategic-leaders

61. We put our personal label on people and things

Stossel, John / Kendal, Kristina (2006): The Psychology of Stereotypes.
http://abcnews.go.com/2020/story?id=2442521&page=1

62. Profound relaxation improves your ability to focus and to be productive

Lehrer, Jonah (2012): The Virtues of Daydreaming, in: The New Yorker.
https://www.newyorker.com/tech/frontal-cortex/the-virtues-of-daydreaming

63. Millions of grey cells only get activated when you switch off

Raichle, Marcus E. (2010): The Brain's Dark Energy, in: Scientific American, March 2010.
https://www2.warwick.ac.uk/fac/sci/dcs/research/combi/seminars/raichle_braindarkenergy_sciam2010.pdf

64. Mind wandering helps you become more creative and productive

Baird, Benjamin / Smallwood, Jonathan / Mrazek, Michael D (2012): Inspired by Distraction. Mind Wandering Facilitates Creative Incubation, in: Psychological Science, Vol 23, Issue 10, pp.1117–1122.
https://doi.org/10.1177/0956797612446024

65. We are much better at detecting other people's faults than our own.

Haidt, Jonathan (2006). The Happiness Hypothesis. Finding Modern Truth in Ancient Wisdom.

66. Our habits are cemented into our brain's neural pathways

Seger, Carol A. / Spiering, Brian J. (2011): A Critical Review of Habit Learning and the Basal Ganglia, in: Frontiers in Systems Neuroscience. 5:66

67. The neurological structures of old habits remain in our brains

Duhigg, Charles (2012): The Power of Habit. Why We Do What We Do in Life and Business. Chapter 1, p. 20.